City of Bradford Metropolitan District Council

Arts, Museums and Libraries Division

City *of*

BRADFORD
METROPOLITAN DISTRICT COUNCIL

Cartwright Hall Art Gallery and its Collections

Edited by

Nima Poovaya-Smith

and

Christine Hopper

A publication to celebrate

Bradford's Centenary Year as a City

and

The 50th Year of Independence

for

India and Pakistan

and

The Gallery of Transcultural Arts

1997

Project funded by:

THE WOLFSON FOUNDATION

(Front and back cover)
LUBNA CHOWDHARY (born 1964)
Cartwright Hall 1995
(From **Bradford City** a series of 9 architectural landmarks)
Stoneware glazes with oxides 32 x 31 x 18 cm

Funded from the proceeds of National Lottery through the Arts Council of England

(Inside front cover)
WILLIAM ROBERTS (1895-1980)
Jockeys/The Paddock 1928
Oil on canvas 122.5 x 92.5 cm

Presented by the Contemporary Art Society

(Inside back cover)
DANTE GABRIEL ROSSETTI (1828-1882)
Study for the head of the Dead Beatrice in the painting
"Dante's Dream on the day of the death of Beatrice" 1871
Chalk on paper 57 x 51 cm

ISBN No 0 946657 47 5

Printed June 1997

Designed and produced by Primary Colour, Bradford

Printed by Steffprint, Keighley

ACKNOWLEDGEMENTS

Brij Bhasin

Priti Bhasin

Mohinder Singh Chana

Salima Hashmi

Shoiab Hashmi

Robert Hopper

Patricia Kattenhorn

Mahmud Khan

Barry Mazur

Jamnaben Mistry

Howard Mruczek

Mrs A. M. Poovaya

Robert Skelton

P.L.R. Smith

Mrs P.K.Sood

Susan Stronge

Dr M.I.Waley

The majority of the photography has been
undertaken by Richard Littlewood

Unless otherwise stated all illustrations
are from the collections of
Bradford Art Galleries and Museums

CONTENTS

Foreword

Cllr Barry Thorne

An Introduction to Cartwright Hall Art Gallery

P. W. G. Lawson

From the Insular to the International

Christine Hopper

Keys to the Magic Kingdom

Nima Poovaya-Smith

Unsung Heroes: The International Print Collection

Caroline Krzesinska

FOREWORD

It gives me particular pleasure to introduce this catalogue **Cartwright Hall Art Gallery and its Collections** since it commemorates several events. It celebrates the fact that 1997 is not only Bradford's Centenary year as a city but also the Golden Jubilee of the Independence of India and Pakistan. It marks the launch of the Transcultural Gallery with its beautiful displays drawn from the permanent collection. It also marks the coming of age of the transcultural collection since Bradford is now the possessor of the largest collection of contemporary South Asian art in the country. What is equally important is the way in which the transcultural collections have been made an integral part of the permanent collection. This lavishly illustrated catalogue testifies to that. It provides us with an introduction to Cartwright Hall, a magnificent building in its own right, and its Fine and Decorative Art collections in a manner that embraces the Western and the Eastern holdings as a whole.

Bradford Art Galleries and Museums owes a debt of gratitude to many organisations and individuals that have made possible both the transcultural gallery and thereby this catalogue. I would particularly like to thank Heritage Lottery Fund, the Arts Council Lottery and the Wolfson Foundation whose generous grants made possible the refurbishment of the gallery and the commissioning of important works of art. The National Art Collections Fund, the Museums and Galleries Commission/Victoria and Albert Museum Purchase Grant Fund and the Henry Moore Foundation have been extremely supportive of our drive to collect ambitiously within the area of transcultural arts. The recent acquisition of **Turning the world inside out** by Anish Kapoor is a considerable coup for Bradford. The collaboration between the Institute of International Visual Arts and Cartwright Hall Art Gallery over the commissioning of work from Avtarjeet Dhanjal and Zarina Bhimji has been particularly rewarding and I hope this relationship will continue to grow and flourish. The Arts Council of England, the Crafts Council and Yorkshire and Humberside Arts, as usual, have extended enthusiastic advice and support towards the development of the transcultural gallery and I would like to thank all these organisations.

I would like to commend the staff of Cartwright Hall for all their efforts in realising this project. The City of Bradford Metropolitan District Council views accessibility to and ownership of Council services as a central plank of its general philosophy. Therefore developing new audiences is vital to Bradford Art Galleries and Museums and it is our hope that the transcultural gallery will be an important catalyst in this process. I hope you will enjoy both reading this catalogue and visiting Cartwright Hall Art Gallery.

Councillor Barry Thorne

Chair, Community & Leisure Sub-Committee

EDITORS' NOTE

Cartwright Hall Art Gallery and its Collections examines a building that is an architectural gem, in its own right, and a collection that is lively, occasionally quirky and unusual.

One of our main concerns is to present the works illustrated in a manner that reflects thematic, schematic and other commonalities, rather than following strictly chronological or media-based lines. This is particularly true of the second colour section. For instance the idea of water as regenerative and life-affirming is a common thread in David Hockney's **Le Plongeur**, Howard Hodgkin's **David's Pool** and Saleem Arif's **Vessel of Vitality**, which is why the three images have been grouped together. Sylvat Aziz's **Exodus Lahore** and Lowry's **Industrial Landscape** have been placed together, although, on the surface, they reflect very different concerns. One depicts the pulverisation caused by the forcible partition of a country, the other the challenge of urbanisation. Both works depict overwhelming realities by reducing the human figure to specks, dwarfed either by the tragedy of a fragmenting country or a soulless urbanisation.

The gold and silver objects, regardless of their scale, often have a narrative or sculptural content that is quite unexpected. The 19th century pierced-work gold plaque depicting a scene from one of the two principal Hindu epics **The Ramayana**, is an exquisite miniature sculpture, complete with a Shiva lingam and an image of the patron king in the corner. The silver shank or shell and the parrot-feeder combine a ritual or practical use with wonderfully strong form and ornamentation.

Loretta Braganza and Henry Pim produce pots that have a similarly sculptural yet two-dimensional quality. Both subvert any practical function. Sarbjit Natt's **Mughal** and Fahmida Shah's **Untitled** are essentially paintings using sumptuous silks rather than canvas or paper as their surface. Sometimes images have been juxtaposed because of similar rhythms of form or line. This has made the assembling of the catalogue an exhilarating and releasing experience. There is seldom the opportunity to combine such a variety of media, form and content; the edges have blurred nicely.

The increasingly international thrust of the collections, be it in contemporary art or calligraphy from the Muslim world, bring it to life and create interest for a wider cross-section of the public.

Nima Poovaya-Smith
Christine Hopper

An Introduction to Cartwright Hall Art Gallery

HISTORICAL BACKGROUND

Cartwright Hall was built as a result of the generosity of Samuel Cunliffe Lister (1815-1906), who was created Lord Masham in 1892. The son of a prominent local family, his father was a wealthy mill owner and one of Bradford's first MPs. Samuel Cunliffe Lister amassed his own fortune through the development of new textile technology, and in 1873 he completed the rebuilding of Manningham Mills, an elegant and gigantic mill complex high above the Bradford valley. Lord Masham made a major contribution towards the development of the textile industry in Yorkshire, and was one of the people who generated Bradford's enormous late Victorian and Edwardian wealth. He was a noted philanthropist and in 1870 he sold Manningham Hall, his family home and the surrounding fifty-three acres of ground to the Bradford Corporation for £40,000, although it had been valued at twice that amount. This land was used to create a public park, now called Lister Park.

In 1838 Samuel Cunliffe Lister and his brother took over the management of Manningham Mills from their father. A few years later, Lister went into partnership with Isaac Holden (1807-1897); both men had an enthusiasm and aptitude for technical innovation and applied their skills to solving the problems of the mechanisation of woolcombing. The result of their endeavours was the invention of the Square Motion Comb. Lister took out an independent patent for such a comb in 1848, although an earlier patent had been taken out jointly by him with Holden.

The partnership between Lister and Holden was terminated in 1858. They continued to modify the Square Motion Comb independently, acquiring considerable wealth in the process. In 1872 they quarrelled openly as to which of them had perfected the Square Motion Comb. This dispute continued until 1886, conducted through a series of acrimonious exchanges in the local newspapers.

In 1898, after Holden's death, Lord Masham offered £40,000 to Bradford Corporation to build Cartwright Hall on the site of Manningham Hall, which was to be demolished. The new building was to be a purpose-built art gallery and museum. He perhaps hoped to avoid controversy by proferring recognition to Dr Edmund Cartwright (1743-1823), whose woolcombing machine had been the basis of later developments and to whom Lord Masham said he owed his own success. The gift was accepted with alacrity by the Corporation, as the old Art Gallery and Museum in Darley Street established in 1879 had become inadequate. The new building was also to double as municipal reception rooms. In 1904, just before the opening of Cartwright Hall, one of the plaques depicting a woolcomb in operation, was removed from the base of Lord Masham's statue, supposedly to alter it for greater `scientific accuracy'. It was replaced with a plaque depicting the Square Motion Comb, associated with Lord Masham. In this way, he staked his definitive claim to its invention.

The Competition

Cartwright Hall was to be a purpose-built art gallery and museum, and in 1898 a nationwide design competition was organised. Alfred Waterhouse, RA (1830-1905), an eminent Victorian architect responsible for the design of major buildings such as the Natural History Museum in London, was appointed assessor. Three concepts were to be embodied in the design of Cartwright Hall. Firstly the building had to be a memorial and hence monumental; secondly, it had to be suitable for civic entertainments; and thirdly, it had to serve as a museum and art gallery.

The Victorian age was characterised by a diversity of architectural styles, but two main strands can be discerned. These are the revived Gothic and Classical, both of which styles were employed for various civic and secular projects. The Gothic style was used for the new Houses of Parliament, various London railway stations and new town halls, such as City Hall in Bradford. The Classical style was used for similar projects, such as the Town Hall in Halifax, the Victoria and Albert Museum in London, and St. George's Hall in Bradford, demonstrating in its many faces its `Greek', `Roman', `Renaissance' and `Italianate' qualities.

By the 1890s, the early 18th century English Baroque style of Wren, Vanbrugh and Hawksmoor was being revived and reinvigorated by progressive English architects. The number of Baroque-inspired buildings chosen for civic ventures in the closing years of the century indicates the growing identification of its grandeur with municipal virtues.

The ample funds, the picturesque site and the nature of the competition made the Cartwright Hall project very attractive and 117 entries were received. The design that fused the three requirements in the best manner, and kept within the costing was submitted by J. W. Simpson and E. J. Milner Allen of London. In May 1899, they were awarded the commission. The architects' previous experience of this type of building had been on a much larger scale - the Glasgow Art Galleries and Museums at Kelvingrove, built between 1897-1899, at a cost of £300,000 in a style very similar to that proposed for Cartwright Hall.

Shortly after work began in Bradford, Allen retired. Sir John William Simpson took sole control and closely supervised building activities over the next four years. Lord Masham had specified that the site of the former Manningham Hall was to provide the ground area for Cartwright Hall. Simpson and Allen adjusted the transverse axis of the building in their plans, so that the site was brought into line with the proposed site for the statue of Sir Titus Salt, another major entrepreneur and philanthropist, at the top of the carriage drive. However, this was to present one of the first stumbling blocks to the construction of the building, which was to take four years. The Boer war, spiralling costs of materials and labour, strikes, freak weather conditions and structural problems in the site and the materials themselves delayed the opening by over two years. The building costs by 1900 were estimated at £55,000 rather than the original £40,000.

Henry Fehr (1867-1940), a distinguished sculptor and graduate of the Royal Academy Schools was commissioned to execute a large statue of Dr Cartwright in marble, for the sum of £1,200. The statue shows Cartwright in his academic gown, as a Fellow of Magdalen College, a clergyman, as well as an inventor, wearing the knee breeches and silver-buckled shoes of the eighteenth century. Decorative carving on the building itself was being carried out by Alfred Broadbent of Chelsea who had actually been born in Shipley, near Bradford.

Simpson produced plans for the grounds of Cartwright Hall at an estimated cost of £6,000; with imposing terraces on the Manningham Lane side and balustrading and ornamental gates in keeping with the architectural character of the Hall, they promised to be as impressive as the building itself.

The opening date was finally set for Wednesday, 13th April 1904. The cost of the Hall was over £70,000, exclusive of furnishings, and far in excess of the revised estimate of 1900. On 24th March, Lord Masham paid his last visit of inspection before the opening ceremony. For the first time, he appeared with a footman, explaining: "I feel now as if I am getting old" *Daily Argus*. The statue of Dr Cartwright had been completed and was transported to Bradford in triumph, having won first place in the Royal Academy sculpture section for 1902.

On the day before the opening ceremony, the joiners were still finishing the oak floors and the statue of Dr Cartwright was being positioned, while Simpson made a final inspection of the building. On the day of the opening Lord Masham was escorted through the festively decorated centre of town by a large contingent of local Councillors and dignitaries. In spite of heavy rain the roads were crowded with cheering citizens as the party drove along Manningham Lane in the Lord Mayor's carriage to Lister Park. Local rifle volunteers lined the carriage drive up to the Hall, and a baize carpet had been laid out. The sun came out as the carriage arrived, welcomed by another group of dignitaries. When the formal act of unlocking the door began, it was discovered that the ornate key specially made for the occasion, and designed by Simpson, had been left behind. An everyday key was hastily produced to complete the ceremony.

The Architecture of Cartwright Hall

The design of Cartwright Hall and the use of the Baroque style conveys a sense of function, monumentality and civic pride - all three requirements of the proposed design. The Baroque style was first developed in early 17th century Italy, evolving from the architectural experiments of Michelangelo and consolidated by the work of Bernini. It is a classically based style, but freely uses stylistic motifs and groupings of architectural masses, to provide drama and a sense of movement. The static and serene nature of purist Classical architecture, with its emphasis on balanced proportion and detail, is alien to the Baroque spirit. Baroque buildings are sculptural masses, usually conceived in the round with the exterior decoration integrated in the overall design.

Facing almost south, the main entrance epitomises this sculptural quality, sweeping over the carriage drive and enfolding the visitor. This sense of drama highlights its ceremonial and monumental function. The most decorative feature is the central tower forming the porch with an open arcade crowned and decorated with ten symbolic figures. Two obelisks rise on either side. The dome adds a vertical thrust to the building, juxtaposed with the horizontal movement of the main body of the building, thus creating a dramatic tension. The facades are decorated with coupled Ionic columns and pilasters; the columns being used in pairs at the front of the porch to project it forwards and on the end-bays, coupled with pilasters on the outside, to also project the bays of the building forward and level with the entrance.

The inner bays are recessed and flattened to appear somewhat static, by the use of pilasters. The columns and pilasters extend from basement level to roof level. No windows appear on the upper storey as the art galleries are top-lit. The skyline is punctuated by the turrets, set back from the south face on either side of the main tower. They balance the vertical and horizontal thrusts of the building, so indicative of the complexity of its rhythmic massing. This is also extended to the other three facades.

On the north side, two entrances are situated on either side of the apse that houses the Sculpture Hall, with two external stone staircases from the entrance that were originally intended for the everyday use of the public. Venetian windows on this side of the building light the interior Sculpture Hall and staircases.

The sumptuousness and grandeur of the building is greatly increased by the textural contrast between the heavily rusticated stone of the basement level and the beautifully worked ashlars of the upper storeys. It is a recreation of a French-based Baroque manner that is rarely seen in England. The accomplishment with which this is used establishes the Hall as a considerable architectural achievement and places it, stylistically, firmly in the Edwardian period.

The Exterior Decorative Motifs

The sheer scale of Cartwright Hall and its conception as a sculptural mass, has tended to diminish the impact of the decorative detailing carved on the exterior of the building which has both an individual quality and symbolic content.

The south front of the Hall with its impressive entrance, dominated by the silhouette of the tower, has always been regarded as the main facade of the building, and it was originally intended solely for the use of guests at civic functions. In view of this special status, it was natural that Simpson should concentrate on providing impressive decorative features to enhance its appearance. The final ornamental scheme applied to the tower was decided only at a comparatively late stage in the construction of the Hall and was the result of a succession of changes made after the publication of the original plan in 1899. On the upper part of the lower stage of the tower are six figures, depicting Art, Literature, Music, Architecture, Sculpture and Drama. Roughly-hewn stones were built into the tower to support the sculpture.

Four other allegorical figures allude more closely to the source of the city's prosperity and its civic virtues. They are important features in the architectural effect from whatever point of view the tower is viewed. The figures on the south side of the tower symbolise Spinning, a woman holding in her hands a distaff, and Commerce, who holds in her hands the emblematic model of a ship. On the north side of the tower, one figure with her hand on the hilt of a sword (who might well be Joan of Arc) represents Fortitude while the other symbolises Abundance.

Bradford had been accorded official city status as recently as 1897. The construction of Cartwright Hall was the most significant civic venture undertaken since that date, and it seemed appropriate for the architect to express the city's pride by giving the building a local context. The mural decorations were to combine the coats of arms of several well-known local families. They were contained in panels measuring fourteen feet by eight feet and were richly and delicately embellished with foliage.

Proposals regarding these coats of arms were criticised at the design stage. The *Daily Argus* reported the unfavourable response of Labour representatives on the Council to the designs, under the headline *The Cartwright Hall - Another Socialist Objection*: "Mr J Hayhurst submitted that there were several names suggested which they as a Corporation had no great reason to be proud of, or to think very kindly of. It seemed to him that the owners of some of the names which were to be inscribed at the Memorial Hall had done very well out of the people, and out of the Bradford Corporation. Was the institution, he asked, to be erected to the perpetuation of ancient customs, or was it to be an institution in which modern ideas were introduced to the carrying out of modern ends? He thought they could very well afford to forget some of those men of the past, whose only qualifications were that they were the sons of their fathers." These ideas received some support within the Committee, but were outvoted. The coat of arms of the City of Bradford and that of Lord Masham, appropriately enough, appear on the south front.

Other motifs, such as the delicately modelled little cherubs heads supporting the blank escutcheons, repeating laurel wreaths above the windows, and the festoons of fruit carved in high-relief, help to create an authentic Baroque atmosphere. Considerable claims were made for the quality of the completed carving, and the *Bradford Daily Telegraph* handbook said of Broadbent's work: "The enrichments, internally and externally, are superb, so much so that one may venture to say, without fear of contradiction, that nowhere in the North of England have we such a display of stone carving". At the opening ceremony Simpson said that the Hall was "the finest building in Europe of its kind .... (with) the finest carving in the world".

The Interior Arrangement of the Hall

Simpson's success in the Cartwright Hall competition was gained, at least in part, because of the effectiveness of his design for the interior arrangement. His plans were seen as offering the most satisfactory practical solution to the stated requirement for a building capable of being used for large-scale civic functions, as well as an art gallery and museum. The competition assessor and the Committee, because of the requirements of the civic dimension of the building, regarded lay-out, the circulation route between the various rooms, and cloak-room provision, as being important criteria in the selection of the winning design. However, following criticism of the design at the Museums Association Conference held in Bradford in 1902, the emphasis shifted towards the building's function as an art gallery and museum, and space originally intended as cloak-rooms, was redesignated as galleries.

The interior of the building was designed to reflect the exterior, and shares with it its Baroque grandeur. The visitor to the Hall passes up the entrance steps, and is confronted by the great Baroque space of the apsed Sculpture Hall, framed by imposing coupled columns. Access to the upper floor is by either one of a pair of grand, and carefully designed, staircases.

These particularly impressed commentators at the time of the opening of the Hall. The *Bradford Daily Telegraph* correspondent wrote "even in passing onto the first floor the visitor continues to have a full sense of the presence of the statuary and the beautiful architectural effects .... one has to freely admit that in his endeavour to keep the various parts of the interior in perceptible touch with each other, so as to give the greatest possible effect to the surroundings, the architect has been signally successful".

The first floor central area, with its massive coupled Corinthian columns, its pilasters and heavily moulded vaulted ceiling is, like the Sculpture Hall, a superbly architectonic space with Fehr's marble sculpture of Dr Edmund Cartwright acting as a centre-piece.

The two galleries adjacent to the central area are flanked by the large east and west galleries and in combination with the adjacent passages, make it possible for the visitor to walk through all the galleries without retracing his or her steps. This is particularly useful on busy visitor days. The large east gallery was used on civic occasions as a banqueting hall. All the upstairs galleries were fitted with picture rails specially designed by Simpson, and lit from above. This arrangement provided for good lighting, and maximum wall space for the hanging of pictures.

The ground floor galleries concentrated on the art gallery and museum rather than the civic function, and housed displays of Art, Archaeology, Social History and Natural Sciences. Other parts of the building, principally the basement, contained storage for the collections, offices, and the cafe and catering facilities.

The interior decoration and fitments reflect the exterior in style, mood and sumptuousness. The floors in the Sculpture Hall and main ground floor passageways are laid with black Belgian and white Sicilian marble. Floors in all other public areas of the building were laid with Indiana oak planks.

The panelling in the East gallery upstairs that was used as a Banqueting Hall was made from American Black Walnut, which when polished, produced a singularly opulent effect. The same material was used for the doors, dados, and window-frames in the building. The lock escutcheons and door handles used in the public areas are outstanding in their own right, and their decoration of sinuous lines and monograms reflect the influence of the Art Nouveau movement. Decorative bronze light fittings were a feature of the Hall and some of these have been restored and placed in the East gallery. It is hoped that others which have survived can be reinstated in the future, particularly those used in the Sculpture Hall, which are embellished with finely-wrought cherubs. The plasterwork cornices and mouldings in the Sculpture Hall and the First Floor Central Area are elaborate, and are in the same massy style as the rest of the building.

The interior of the building was originally painted in the light colours popular at the time for Baroque interiors, with details such as cornices and mouldings picked out in white. These colours were intended to contribute towards the sense of light and spaciousness within the building.

Some of the galleries on the upper floor had wall-coverings of terracotta coloured silk, manufactured by Messrs Lister and Co., at Manningham Mills. A writer in the *Yorkshire Daily Observer* noted that the silk was "a shade which had been found to yield satisfactory results in one of the finest Parisian art galleries, and which had been adapted in Bradford after much consideration". This illustrates again the care and thought that went into the design of the Hall, and the determination of the architect and the Council that the building should be one of the finest of its type in Europe.

Summary

Simpson's design incorporated several fairly recent technological developments. One of these was the use of load-bearing structural steel within the building concealed by decorative plasterwork. It was an important element in ensuring that the floors could take, not only the weight of heavy exhibits, but also large crowds of visitors.

The heating and ventilating system was innovatory for its period. Air was drawn down a large shaft from roof-level to the basement by a fan, and through hessian cleaning screens. In winter, the air was passed over a battery of pipes heated by steam provided by boilers. The heated air was then driven by the fan into what the *Yorkshire Daily Observer* handbook described as "a perfect catacomb of ducts and tunnels ....[which] .... ramify into numberless flues which run through the internal walls and communicate with every room". As the air cooled it was expelled from the building through ducts. In summer, the system circulated cool air around the building. This system was particularly effective, as it not only ensured a fairly constant temperature throughout the various galleries, which was important for the preservation of exhibits such as paintings, but also obviated the need for installing radiators in the galleries. This last point was important in conservation terms since concentrated heat is inimical to the health of works of art, particularly paintings. The system was modified and refined in 1980-1 when a new air handling plant, boilers and controls were installed. This was partly to replace worn out equipment, but also enabled a more efficient control of humidity and temperature so important to works of art.

Another relatively recent development incorporated into the design was electric lighting, comparatively new in 1904. However, since certain categories of object, notably works on paper such as drawings, watercolours and prints can be severely damaged by exposure to natural light, it has become necessary to install blinds in some galleries to exclude or control daylight. This has meant the introduction of modern lighting fitments, such as spotlights and fluorescent tubes.

In conclusion, the reasons for the building of Cartwright Hall Art Gallery were complex. The 18th and, in particular, the 19th century had seen a growing enthusiasm in Western Europe for the establishment of art museums. These not only celebrated the civilisation and culture of particular societies but also acted as a vital educational resource. The cities that had expanded mightily in the first half of the 19th century, as a consequence of the wealth generated by industry and commerce, began to increasingly propagate a civic gospel in the latter half of the 19th century. The city fathers sought to establish civilised policies which reflected the community values and artistic excellence of the Renaissance cities of Italy. These enthusiasms, together with the growing emphasis on popular education, led to the opening of the first art gallery and museum in the centre of Bradford in 1879. The building of Cartwright Hall reinforced and expanded this particular strand of culture.

The building itself is a consummate architectural achievement. Through its sophistication, grandeur and technical confidence, it reflects the cultural tradition of late Victorian and Edwardian society. It is bold and assertive but also subtle and full of nuances. In an appropriate sylvan landscape setting, it not only expressed the confidence of the society that built it but also the inclusive nature of that society.

The building in terms of its function as an art gallery and museum has stood the test of time remarkably well. All art museums have two sides to them. One is the collection of material from particular cultural traditions, caring for it and conserving it. The other is showing it to as wide a public as possible and not just to a specialist audience. The public face includes temporary exhibitions of borrowed material and the interpretation of the permanent collections to a wide cross-section of society. Cartwright Hall has proved to be an immensely flexible space. The building still meets the basic requirements of providing a secure repository for often valuable material and appropriate spaces for very varied exhibitions. The evolution of Bradford communities has been mirrored by an evolution within the building itself and the roles it fulfils for the public of Bradford and beyond.

P. W. G. Lawson
Head of Arts, Museums and Libraries

NUDRAT AFZA (born 1955)
Photograph of Cartwright Hall 1996
48 x 32 cm
*Funded from the proceeds of the National Lottery through the
Arts Council of England*

NUDRAT AFZA (born 1955)
Photograph of Cartwright Hall 1996
48 x 32 cm
*Funded from the proceeds of the National Lottery through the
Arts Council of England*

Sculpture Court 1997
Cartwright Hall

Gallery 2 1997
Cartwright Hall

Gallery 4 1997
Cartwright Hall

Brass door fitting
Cartwright Hall
Designed by the architect J.W.Simpson and made by Gibbons of Wolverhampton

ROBERT WYLIE (1839-1877)
A Breton Sorceress c.1872
Oil on canvas 91.5 x 119.5 cm
Presented by the family of the late Alfred Harris

THE HON. JOHN COLLIER (1850-1934)
**The Right Hon. Samuel Cunliffe Lister
(Baron Masham of Swinton)** 1901
Oil on canvas 127 x 102 cm
*Presented by the Lord Mayor, William C.Lupton,
for the City of Bradford*

C.J.STANILAND (1838-1916)
The Emigrant Ship 1880s
Oil on canvas 104 x 176 cm
Presented by Frederick Priestman

JAMES LOBLEY (1828-1888)
The Dole, Stow Church c.1867
Oil on panel 50.5 x 71 cm

ALFRED ELMORE (1815-1881)
The Invention of the Combing Machine 1862
Oil on canvas 100 x 141 cm

CHARLES LIDDERDALE (1831-1895)
Rejected Addresses 1876
Oil on canvas 128 x 86.5 cm
Presented by Sir Frederick Ackroyd

MORRIS, MARSHALL, FAULKNER & CO
The Tomb of Tristram and Isoude 1862
Designed by Edward Burne-Jones to illustrate the story of
Tristram and Isoude from Malory's **Morte d'Arthur**

MORRIS, MARSHALL, FAULKNER & CO
King Arthur and Sir Lancelot 1862
Designed by William Morris to illustrate the story of Tristram
and Isoude from Malory's **Morte d'Arthur**

MORRIS, MARSHALL, FAULKNER & CO
Weeping Angels 1870
Designed by Edward Burne-Jones for the east window of St
James's Church, Brighouse
Presented in 1972

21

FORD MADOX BROWN (1821-1893)
The First Translation of the Bible into English: Wycliffe Reading his Translation of the New Testament to his Protector, John of Gaunt, Duke of Lancaster, in the Presence of Chaucer and Gower, his Retainers 1847-8, 1859-61
Oil on canvas 119.5 x 153.5 cm

FORD MADOX BROWN (1821-1893)
A small first sketch for "The First Translation of the Bible into English: Wycliffe Reading his Translation of the New Testament to his Protector, John of Gaunt, Duke of Lancaster, in the Presence of Chaucer and Gower, his Retainers" 1847
Oil on panel 18 x 25 cm
Purchased with the assistance of the Victoria and Albert Museum Purchase Grant Fund and the National Art Collections Fund

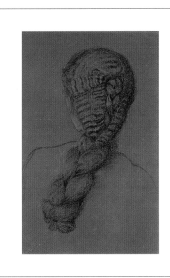

FORD MADOX BROWN (1821-1893)
Romeo and Juliet 1876
Pen, ink and black chalk on paper 71 x 52.5 cm
Presented by Asa Lingard

EDWARD BURNE-JONES (1833-1898)
Hair studies c.1890
Chalk on paper
Presented by W. T. Vint

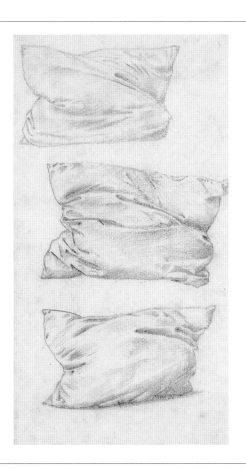

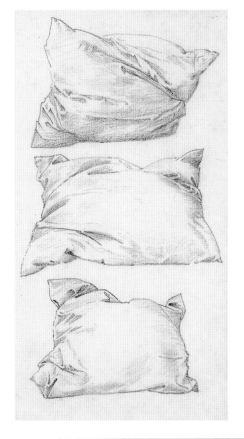

EDWARD BURNE-JONES (1833-1898)
Cushion studies c.1884
Chalk on paper
Bequest of Mrs Constance Rea

DANTE GABRIEL ROSSETTI (1828-1882)
La Donna della Finestra 1870
Pastel on paper 85 x 72 cm
Presented by Asa Lingard

FREDERICK HALL (1860-1948)
The Drinking Pool c.1898
Oil on canvas 73.5 x 160.5 cm

HENRY HERBERT LA THANGUE (1859-1929)
The Connoisseur 1887
Oil on canvas 114 x 160 cm
Presented by Mrs V.H.Mitchell

HENRY HERBERT LA THANGUE (1859-1929)
In the Orchard c.1893
Oil on canvas 83 x 72.5 cm

GEORGE CLAUSEN (1852-1944)
The Boy and the Man c.1909
Oil on canvas 197.5 x 164 cm

WRIGHT BARKER (1863-1941)
Circe c.1889
Oil on canvas 138 x 199.5 cm
Presented by W.H.North

HERBERT DRAPER (1864-1920)
The Golden Fleece 1904
Oil on canvas 155 x 272.5 cm

EDWIN LONG (1829-1891)
An Egyptian Feast 1877
Oil on canvas 189 x 381 cm
Presented by Mrs Janet Lund

THE HON. JOHN COLLIER (1850-1934)
Queen Guinevere's Maying c.1897
Oil on canvas 180.5 x 121 cm
Presented by the daughters of the late William Rawlings

JAMES WARD (1769-1859)
Gordale Scar 1813
Oil on canvas 76 x 102 cm

JOHN ATKINSON GRIMSHAW (1836-1893)
Fianella / Fiametta c.1883
Oil on canvas 61 x 46 cm
*Purchased with the assistance of the National Art Collections
Fund and the Friends of Bradford Art Galleries and Museums*

GEORGE ROMNEY (1734-1802)
Portrait of Dr James Ainslie of Kendal c.1765-80
Oil on canvas 145 x 121 cm

THOMAS GAINSBOROUGH (1727-1788)
Portrait of Sir Francis Basset early 1760s
Oil on canvas 128 x 102.5 cm

JOSHUA REYNOLDS (1723-1792)
Master Thomas Lister, "The Brown Boy" 1764
Oil on canvas 231 x 147.5 cm
Presented by H.M.Treasury

GIORGIO VASARI (1511-1574)
The Holy Family with St John
Oil on panel 141 x 113 cm
Purchased with the assistance of the Victoria and Albert
Museum Purchase Grant Fund

PHILIP WILSON STEER (1860-1942)
The End of the Chapter 1911
Oil on canvas 120.5 x 143 cm

GUIDO RENI (1575-1642)
The Flight into Egypt
Oil on canvas 160 x 129.3 cm
*Purchased with the assistance of the Victoria and Albert
Museum Purchase Grant Fund*

BERTRAM PRIESTMAN (1868-1951)
The Heart of the West Riding 1916
Oil on canvas 115.5 x 184 cm
Presented by the artist

FROM THE INSULAR
TO THE INTERNATIONAL

BRADFORD ART MUSEUM 1879-1904

Bradford's first museum venture in 1879 differed little from other art museums springing up in provincial towns all over the country. Situated in a large toplit room above the Free Library, it was part of the Kirkgate Market building erected six years before in Darley Street in the centre of Bradford. A small group of exhibits was quickly donated by local collectors; a suit of Japanese armour given by Edward, the eldest son of Sir Titus Salt, and a picture **Gipsie's Encampment** painted and donated by a local artist and former painter and decorator, John Gelder. In true Art Museum style, fossils and pots jostled for space with war relics from the Sudan battlefield. Purchases were of a didactic nature; electrotype reproductions of silver and gold items from the South Kensington Museum and plaster casts of classical statuary. Art students of this period were still expected to learn by copying the art of the past, rather than working from nature as advocated by Ruskin.

The picture today, almost one hundred and twenty years later, could not be more dramatically different. The collections have expanded, almost dizzyingly, in a number of directions. Bradford, like all museums, has a collecting policy which focuses attention on particular areas. These have varied at different times. Modern British art has formed the nucleus since the 1890s. Since the 1960s, significant purchases have been made of prints by international artists. From the 1980s the collections have taken on an increasingly cosmopolitan thrust. This has resulted in an interesting and varied collection, where the very contemporary Laila Rahman jostles with the visionary, anguished William Blake and the Goan Catholic F N Souza hangs companionably with Bradford's brightest, David Hockney. The dialogue between artists cuts through time and culture, a truly transcultural experience.

Today's displays are very different from that first exhibition in 1879. The pictures selected then had clearly been chosen to suit popular taste. They were described with warm approval in a local newspaper as "honest, healthy English art". [1] The writer proudly declared that "local collectors have not caught the Pre-Raffaelite (sic) and medieval infection". Ironically, this critic was unaware that one of the chief contributors to the exhibition was a prominent patron and admirer of Dante Gabriel Rossetti (1828-1882), the most influential of the founders of the Pre-Raphaelite Brotherhood in 1849. Walter Dunlop had both bought directly from Rossetti and, in 1862, commissioned a set of thirteen stained glass panels from the newly established firm of Morris, Marshall, Faulkner and Co.

The panels illustrated the doomed love of Tristram and Isoude from Malory's **Morte d'Arthur** and were installed in Dunlop's newly enlarged home Harden Grange, near Bingley. Drawings for the panels were made by artists who included Rossetti, Burne-Jones, Ford Madox Brown and William Morris himself. Val Prinsep and Arthur Hughes were also involved with this commission, although their interest in the stained glass medium was to be short-lived. Morris, who supervised the overall scheme, adapted the artists' designs and selected the type and colour of the handmade glass. The design was divided according to the medieval style, by adding lines for the leading that followed and enclosed strong shapes, figures, garments and trees, even baby Tristram has his own lead surround. The medieval flavour is reinforced by the inscribed description incorporated in each panel. The simplicity of each design combines with the flowing lines and rich colours to make a series of beautiful panels, remarkable for their secular subject.

The arrangement of the panels within Harden Grange itself has been the subject of much debate. They were, in all probability, not laid out according to the sequence of the story, but were dotted about the many windows of the entrance porch on the east side of the house for maximum visual effect. The two portrait panels of **King Arthur and Sir Lancelot** and **Queen Guinevere and Isoude**, wife of Tristram do not fit obviously into the story. Both were designed by William Morris and succeed because of the simple beauty of the background which prefigures Morris's later wallpaper and textile designs. After Dunlop's death, the panels were bought for the Bradford collections. Regrettably, the rest of the collection was dispersed and eventually sold to other museums in Britain and the U.S.

Wealthy Bradford merchants and manufacturers were avid art collectors. Many preferred the mediation of dealers rather than exposure to live artists. Dunlop's neighbour in Bingley, John Aldam Heaton (died 1897), was an even more avid collector of works by Rossetti. Indeed, the proliferation of Pre-Raphaelite artworks in Bradford in the 1860s probably owed something to Heaton's influence. Local collectors were generous with their loans but large gifts and bequests were few. Although the Museum did not benefit significantly in terms of being bequeathed large collections from these wealthy collectors, they were important in the sense that they helped transform provincial tastes through their own collections and loans. As patrons of art, some of them had developed warm friendships with prominent, established artists. This had the effect of widening horizons.

Henry Herbert La Thangue (1859-1929), a prominent member of the New English Art Club, the group of artists now more popularly and succintly known as the `British Impressionists', visited Bradford in the 1880s at the invitation of collector John Maddocks whom he had met in Brittany. Bradford was rich territory for a young portrait painter and La Thangue received commissions from most of the Bradford collectors. A prominent manufacturing family, Abraham Mitchell and his son Tom, were particularly generous patrons. La Thangue's arrival inspired the establishment of an amateur/professional group the Arcadian Art Club, evidence of a growing enthusiasm for the arts in Bradford which would eventually lead to public pressure for a grander art gallery.

By the 1890s it had become apparent that the original hope of an Art Museum `equipped' by gifts from the community was not to be fulfilled, even though each catalogue continued to include a `Form of Bequest' outlining the method of making a gift. Bradford decided in 1891 to adopt the Museums Act to enable them to levy a rate to fund purchases for the Art Museum and a Spring exhibition was instituted in 1893. Artists from all over the country were invited to submit their work. The selected works had sometimes already been exhibited in the previous year's Royal Academy exhibition in London. The popularity of the Spring exhibition both with the public and participating artists ensured its survival, for nearly seventy years, into the 1960s.

The first art purchases were made from the 1893 Spring exhibition.   Both artists were members of the Arcadian Art Club.   The choice was made with the assistance of an Advisory Committee, exclusively comprising members of the Arcadian Art Club. The idea of purchasing pictures did not meet with everyone's approval.

The ratepayers did not elect councillors to act as connoisseurs in art, or to purchase pictures with money which was wrung from the pockets of those who could ill afford it. [2]

The most important single thrust of collecting came with these purchases from the Spring exhibitions. La Thangue's **In the Orchard** was a major purchase in 1894, followed quickly by **The Drinking Pool** by Fred Hall (1860-1948) and **The Lemon Tree** by Henry Tuke (1858-1929). A cohesive group of works by the most important British Impressionist artists was quickly assembled to stand alongside an increasing number of large paintings in the Academy tradition culminating in 1902 with the Royal Academy 'Picture of the year', **The Cloister or the World** by Arthur Hacker (1858-1919). There was a growing demand for a new art gallery and museum suitable to Bradford's city status which was to be granted in 1897.

CARTWRIGHT - THE INAUGURAL EXHIBITION 1904

The grand opening of Cartwright Hall took place in 1904, a full two years later than planned. The building itself was inaugurated by Lord Masham in April and opened by the Prince and Princess of Wales the following month with a major exhibition of Fine and Decorative art filling the entire building. The style was similar to that of the Wallace Collection in London, the theme, English Art from Hogarth to the present day.

The manner of exhibiting was to be an effort to show the work of Art in some natural and harmonious arrangement with one another: that is, that the works of art were, as far as possible, to be disposed in the way in which such things are intended to be seen - at home - in something like natural association. [3]

Fine and decorative art items were lent from nationally renowned public and private collections. Lord Masham was particularly generous, with loans of pictures by European artists who had exerted an important influence on the development of English Art - Hobbema, Teniers, Greuze and Rubens. He also loaned a number of pictures by prominent English artists. The Exhibition Committee included collectors who had had a close involvement with the old Art Museum such as John Maddocks and Tom Mitchell. The Committee also included a new generation of collectors with new interests, such as Victor Sichel and his artist son Ernest - and Charles Rothenstein (later Rutherston), and his brother the artist William Rothenstein (1872-1945). Rothenstein and Ernest Sichel had trained together at the Slade School in London in the 1890s.

William Rothenstein chaired the committee of artists selecting the contemporary art section, assisted by Sichel, William Strang and J.M.Swan. As Rothenstein later recalled in his autobiography

We got together what was probably the best exhibition of contemporary art that had ever been held in Yorkshire, not without opposition from Bradford however. They thought we were being too revolutionary. [4]

However, the London bias was noticed and approved in national publications such as *The Athenaeum.*

That exhibition, organised by a London committee... was arranged on lines the very opposite of those followed by the ordinary provincial showman, that is to say, that the endeavour was to make the standard of admission one of artistic excellence rather than one of popularity or academic prestige. [5]

The exhibition made a profit which was spent on furnishing the gallery with works of art. Rothenstein and his friends may have been disappointed that the purchasing continued to be confined to the Spring exhibitions. In spite of this, his interest in the gallery continued and he and his family presented a number of paintings and drawings over the next ten years.

Between the Wars

Purchases continued to be made on the recommendation of the Advisory Committee, still dominated by local collectors such as Arthur Crossland, Wyndham Vint, Asa Lingard and Father O'Connor (who was coincidentally the model for G.K.Chesterton's "Father Brown" stories).

The permanent collection catalogue of 1924 described Bradford's policy of collecting drawings:

By means of sketches and studies in various stages of completion this collection is intended to give students and others some idea of the way in which the artists prepared for their finished work. [6]

Drawings by Rossetti and Burne-Jones fitted this policy admirably and their acquisition was prioritised, creating not only a collection of remarkable drawings but also a record for students of the artist's progress towards a finished work of art. The first gifts were from Wyndham Vint in 1919. These unusual chalk drawings by Burne-Jones of a female models's elaborate, thickly plaited hair were soon augmented by the purchase of drapery and figure studies for Burne-Jones' painting **The Annunciation**. Two studies of the prone figure of Sir Lancelot, clothed and unclothed, further demonstrated the artist's process. Burne-Jones' charmingly quirky studies of cushions, probably made for the Tate's **King Cophetua and the Beggar maid**, were presented only in 1953 but, nonetheless, fit comfortably with the rest of the collection.

Rossetti's studies are more finished, suggesting that they may have been completed to make them saleable to collectors. **La Donna della Finestra** in particular, presented in 1926 by Asa Lingard, is a beautifully executed pastel, the shadowy interior of the room more than indicated with the addition of a quotation from Dante. The **Study for head of Dead Beatrice**, in spite of being monogrammed and dated, is less polished. It was purchased along with other drawings by both Rossetti and Burne-Jones in 1921 from the sale of the collection of Samuel Milne-Milne, a local collector of Pre-Raphaelite drawings who had, before his death, lent generously to the first Cartwright Hall exhibition in 1904.

The Coming of Age exhibition held in 1925 repeated the theme of the inaugural exhibition of 1904 and showed English Art from Hogarth to the present day. Lord Masham's family were again generous with loans of Old Masters. The exhibition also included a large body of Modern British pictures lent by Charles Rutherston. Regrettably, later in the year, he presented his entire collection to Manchester City Art Gallery. The memorial sculpture **Humanity overcoming War** was finally installed in the Sculpture Hall in 1925. Initially commissioned in 1920 from Francis Derwent Wood (1871-1926) as a monument to peace, the violence of the image had caused a major local controversy when first seen in maquette form.

Acquisitions still continued to be made from the Spring exhibition, and these were of variable quality. 1927 saw the first gifts from the Contemporary Art Society, watercolours by Therese Lessore (1885-1945) and David Bomberg (1890-1957), followed in 1935 by Christopher Wood's oil **The Manicure (Portrait of Frosca Munster)** and William Roberts' oil **Jockeys/The Paddock.** The Contemporary Art Society continues to be an important source of contemporary acquisitions for all regional galleries.

THE SWINGING SIXTIES

In 1958 Peter Bird was appointed, the first of a number of Directors from outside Bradford. The exhibitions programme expanded and purchases became more adventurous.

With the arrival of a new Director a survey of the art collections was made and an outline collecting policy prepared to assist in the planned acquisition of suitable works of art. [7]

The Advisory Committee quietly disappeared at this time although approval of the Libraries, Art Gallery and Museums Committee continued to be necessary for purchases. The first purchases of David Hockney's work were made in 1965 from a one-man exhibition at the Lane Gallery in Bradford. **The Hypnotist, Three Kings and a Queen** and **Gretchen and the Snurl**, recent etchings with aquatint were acquired. The purchase of Old Masters was also begun, starting with prints and drawings by Parmigianino, Agostino Carracci, Castiglione and Tiepolo, followed by a small number of paintings such as **The Holy Family with St John** a rare work by the architect and historian Giorgio Vasari (1511-1574). This fine example of the `Mannerist' style with its exaggerated postures and bright colours probably once formed part of an altarpiece. The purchasing policy was noticed in an article in the Sunday Times by John Russell.

In Bradford the look of the City Art Gallery was changed in a mere 18 months by an intelligent buying policy. [8]

John Morley was responsible for laying the initial plans for the British International Print Biennale first held in Bradford in 1968.

Bradford has a strong sense of tradition .....now it is attempting to fuse the old with the new, accepting the fact that new ways of thinking and new ways of living have come to stay....Bradford is creating a new image of and for itself, into which the holding of a major International Print Exhibition fits well. [9]

Regular purchases from each Biennale were to be an important aspect of the development of the collections from 1968 to the end of the 1980s and this is discussed in the essay on the International Print collection. The Hockney collection was augmented in the 1970s with the purchase of two major series of prints illustrating **The Rake's Progress** and **Grimm's Fairy Tales**, continuing the narrative theme seen earlier in **Gretchen and the Snurl.**

The exhibition **East comes West: Five Artists from India and Pakistan** was held in 1971 in association with the Bradford Festival. Works by all five of the artists Ashu Roy, Anwar Shemza, Yunus, Viren Sahai and Balraj Khanna were purchased. In the same year, Sir Joshua Reynolds' important full-length portrait of **Master Thomas Lister, "The Brown Boy"** was allocated to Bradford by H.M.Treasury.

Formerly in the collection of Lord Masham, this magnificent work was commissioned from Reynolds by its first owners, the Listers of Gisburne Park. The young heir to the Gisburne estate is shown in confident pose, handsomely clad in a suit of brown silk with Vandyke collar. His languid stance, leaning on a staff echoes that of the marble copy of the **Apollo Sauroctonos,** which must have been seen by Reynolds during his visit to Rome between 1750-52.

Two important additions were also made to the Hockney collection, the large "Paper Pool" work, **Le Plongeur** and a further important series of prints, **The Blue Guitar** of 1977 in which Hockney pays homage to his hero Picasso. Hockney had read the Wallace Stevens' poem **The Man with the Blue Guitar** which takes as its point of departure Picasso's painting **The Old Guitarist**. In the same year the folio of William Blake's prints illustrating **The Book of Job** was purchased.

In the 1980s, a large collection of work by Jamini Roy (1887-1972) was purchased from a retired army officer who had lived in Bengal in the 1940s and developed a close friendship with the artist. A number of important works by the artist Shanti Panchal (born 1951) were acquired in 1987. This was followed by a major exhibition of his work **Earthen Shades** which toured to several venues in the country. An exhibition of work by Edward Wadsworth (1889-1949) triggered the purchase of the important watercolour **Trees beside River** (1913), the woodcut **Bradford: View of a Town** (1914) and the Black Country drawing **Tipton/Ladle Slag, Tipton Furnaces**. The Contemporary Art Society was again generous with gifts of work by Anish Kapoor and Shirazeh Houshiary. The acquisition of a major piece by Anish Kapoor **Turning the world inside out** has provided a spectacular centrepiece for the Sculpture Court. At the same time, the opening of the gallery of transcultural arts has provided a new focus to the collections.

Bradford's collections policy has always reflected the interests and preoccupations of the day. Through the vision and wisdom - and occasional eccentricity - of its benefactors and curators, the collections have grown from the insular to the international.

Christine Hopper

Assistant Keeper, Fine Art

1 **Bradford Observer**, 29th May 1879 p.5
2 **Bradford Observer**, 14th June 1893 p.6
3 **City of Bradford Exhibition, Catalogue of the Works of Art in the Cartwright Memorial Hall** (1904) Prefatory note by the Director, Butler Wood p.3
4 William Rothenstein, **Men and Memories**, recollections of William Rothenstein volume II, 1900-1922 p.57
5 **The Athenaeum** July 1905 p.24 (article by Count Kessler)
6 **City of Bradford Corporation Art Gallery, Cartwright Memorial Hall**, Illustrated Catalogue of the Permanent Collection of Pictures and other Works of Art (1924) p.69
7 **City of Bradford, Annual Report of the Libraries Art Galleries and Museums Committee** (1958-59) p.22
8 'Culture for a Crisis', article by John Russell in the **Sunday Times**, 7th January 1968
9 **Exhibition Catalogue of the 1st British International Print Biennale**, Bradford (1968). Foreword by Helen Kapp, Exhibition Director p.3

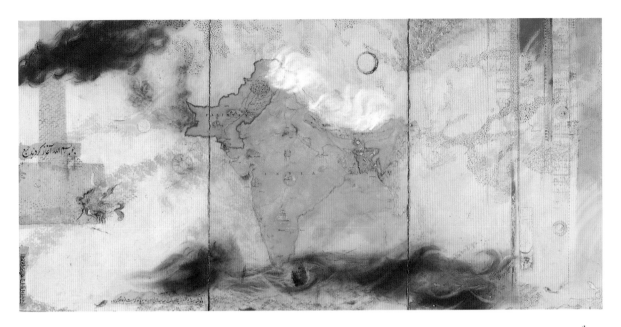

SALIMA HASHMI (born 1942)
Zones of Dreams 1996
Tea wash, gold leaf, acrylic and collage
on paper 152 x 306 cm (triptych)
*Funded from the proceeds of the National
Lottery through the Arts
Council of England*

EDWARD WADSWORTH (1889-1949)
Bradford: View of a Town 1914
Woodcut 15 x 10 cm
*Purchased with the assistance of the Victoria
and Albert Museum Purchase Grant Fund and
the Friends of Bradford Art Galleries and
Museums*
© The estate of Edward Wadsworth
All rights reserved DACS 1997

41

DAVID HOCKNEY (born 1937)
Bolton Junction, Eccleshill 1956
Oil on panel 122 cm x 101.5
Presented by Mrs Taylor
© David Hockney

FRANCIS NEWTON SOUZA (born 1924)
Bradford 1958
Oil on panel 122 x 60.5 cm
Purchased with the assistance of the
MGC/V&A Purchase Grant Fund

AMAL GHOSH (born 1933)
Flight II 1995
Oil on canvas 183 x 152.5 cm
Funded from the proceeds of the National Lottery
through the Arts Council of England

DAVID BOMBERG (1890-1957)
The Chinaman 1921
Watercolour 40.5 x 56 cm
Presented by the Contemporary Art Society

43

ARPANA CAUR (born 1954)
The Embroiderer 1996
Oil on canvas 165 x 137.5 cm
*Funded from the proceeds of the National Lottery through the
Arts Council of England*

CHRISTOPHER WOOD (1901-1930)
The Manicure (Portrait of Frosca Munster) 1929
Oil on canvas 152.5 x 102 cm
Presented by the Contemporary Art Society

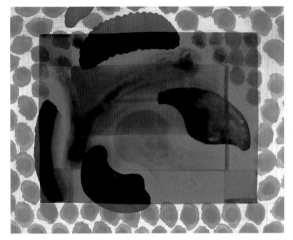

SALEEM ARIF (born 1949)
Vessel of Vitality 1994
Oil on muslin and wood 110 x 160 cm
Funded from the proceeds of the National Lottery through the Arts Council of England

HOWARD HODGKIN (born 1932)
David's Pool 1985
Etching and aquatint with hand-colouring (edition of 100)
64 x 79 cm
Purchased with the assistance of the Victoria and Albert Museum Purchase Grant Fund

DAVID HOCKNEY (born 1937)
Le Plongeur (Paper Pool #18) 1978
Coloured and pressed paper pulp on paper
Two sections each 182 x 213.5 cm
Purchased with the assistance of the Victoria and Albert Museum Purchase Grant Fund
© David Hockney

WILLIAM ROTHENSTEIN (1872-1945)
Self Portrait c.1906
Oil on canvas 102 x 89 cm
Presented by the artist's brother, Charles Rutherston

TOM WOOD (born 1955)
Naked Self Portrait 1978
Acrylic on canvas 61 x 61 cm
Presented by Arthur Haigh

PETER LELY (1618-1680)
Portrait of the artist
Sepia on paper 25 x 19 cm

SUTAPA BISWAS (born 1962)
Housewives with Steak-Knives 1985-86
Pastel & acrylic with xerox collage on paper 274 x 244 cm
Purchased with the assistance of the MGC/V&A Purchase Grant
Fund

GODFRIED SCHALCKEN (1643-1706)
Saint Peter by Candlelight 1700-6
Oil on canvas 61.5 x 48 cm

AMRITA SHER-GIL (1913-1941)
Portrait of a Woman 1939
Watercolour on paper 27 x 18 cm
Presented anonymously

JAMINI ROY (1887-1972)
Panch Kanya 1943-44
Gouache on paper 29.1 x 63.6 cm

JAMINI ROY (1887-1972)
Five Plants 1943-44
Gouache on paper 29.1 x 63.6 cm

PATRICK CAULFIELD (born 1936)
Earthenware 1967
Screenprint on paper (Edition of 75) 53 x 89 cm

SYLVAT AZIZ (born 1954)
Exodus Lahore 1993
Pigment, woodcut, silver foil, dye, henna, etched prints, ink
and rhoplex, collage on paper 122 x 236 cm
Purchased with the assistance of the MGC/V&A Purchase Grant
Fund and the NACF

L.S.LOWRY (1887-1976)
Industrial Landscape (Ashton-under-Lyne) 1952
Oil on canvas 115 x 152.5 cm
By courtesy of the copyright holder, Mrs Carol Ann Danes

TOM WOOD (born 1955)
Portrait of Elaine at the Schlossmuseum 1978
Acrylic on paper 25.5 x 50 cm
Presented by Arthur Haigh

GURMINDER SIKAND (born 1960)
Landscape with Woman and Tree 1994
Watercolour and gouache on paper 30 x 42 cm
Funded from the proceeds of the National Lottery through the
Arts Council of England

ANISH KAPOOR (born 1954)
Untitled 1990
Ink, acrylic and pigment on paper 76.5 x 55 cm
Presented by the Contemporary Art Society

ANTHONY BENJAMIN (born 1931)
Yellow Arch Style 1969
Screenprint (edition of 30) 103 x 72 cm

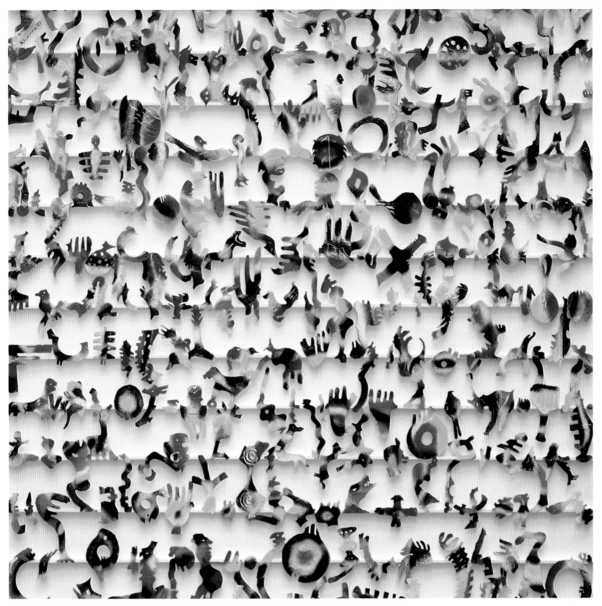

BALRAJ KHANNA (born 1940)
Nursery Rhymes - for Dmitri 1997
Acrylic, card and sand on wood base 183 x 183 cm
Funded from the proceeds of the National Lottery through the
Arts Council of England

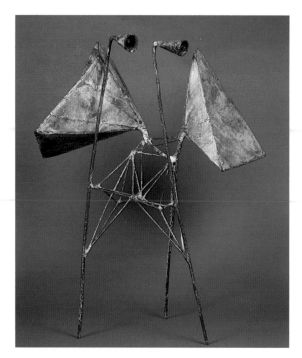

DHRUVA MISTRY (born 1957)
Guardian 1 and Guardian 11 1993
Bronze (edition of 3) 35.5 x 25 x 48 cm
35 x 27 x 47 cm
*Purchased with assistance from the Henry Moore Foundation,
the MGC/V & A Purchase Grant Fund and the NACF*

LYNN CHADWICK (born 1914)
Radar/The Politician 1953
Welded steel and stained plaster 60.5 x 49 x 28 cm
*Purchased with the assistance of the Victoria and Albert
Museum Purchase Fund, the NACF and the Friends of Bradford
Art Galleries and Museums*

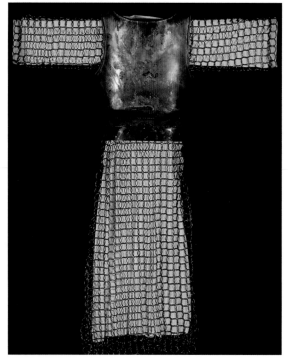

FRANCIS DERWENT WOOD (1871-1926)
Humanity Overcoming War 1925
Serravezza marble 2.5 x 2.1 x 1.4 m
Commissioned in 1921 and completed in 1925

PERMINDAR KAUR (born 1965)
Nightdress 1996
Metal and textile 147 x 107 x 13 cm
*Funded from the proceeds of the National Lottery through the
Arts Council of England*

FRANK DOBSON (1886-1963)
Kneeling Female Nude c.1915
Sandstone 48 x 16 x 21 cm
Purchased with the assistance of the Henry Moore Foundation

Temple Chariot Horse
Painted wood 218 x 215 x 95 cm including base
Tamil Nadu early 20th century

ANISH KAPOOR (born 1954)
Turning the world inside out 1997
Stainless steel 148 x 184 x 188 cm
Purchased with funding from the proceeds of the National Lottery
through the Arts Council of England, the NACF and the Henry
Moore Foundation

UNSUNG HEROES?
THE INTERNATIONAL PRINT COLLECTION

In almost every period of artistic growth printmaking has played a fascinating, and at times crucial, role in the development of ideas. It is perhaps one of the most intriguing and flexible of media at the disposal of artists; it is also one of the most misunderstood. Set alongside the personal, autographic activity of drawing, painting or sculpture, the act of making a print can appear mechanical, distanced as it is from the first brush stroke or pencil mark with which we associate the creative act. A printmaker cannot just reach for a sketchbook or lump of clay when inspiration strikes. Once started, unwanted first thoughts cannot be rubbed or scraped away. It is a medium that requires premeditation and planning and perhaps a particular kind of temperament.

Since the development of the printing press, European prints have been principally involved with the communication of ideas. The process allowed complex images to travel with unprecedented speed around the continent; developments in one artistic centre were transported to another by means of the simple transfer of a drawing onto wood, cut to replicate the black lines of the design and then printed many times. Almost from the start, prints could be seen purely as a means to an end; a tool for teaching and for the dissemination of ideas. A whole army of craftsmen distanced the creators of the original design from the printed outcome. The block cutters, line engravers, printers and publishers produced technically perfect reproductions of religious images, selected glories of the classical world, heroic moments in history and topical political stories to feed an eager market.

Counterbalancing this rather humdrum activity were the works of those artists who were driven by their fascination and curiosity about the creative possibilities of print. Printmaking has frequently allowed craft and concept to complement each other. From Dürer to Hockney, the finest prints have been made by artists who have manipulated and exploited traditional techniques to produce images that are sparklingly innovative, and which reflect their time. For such artists, the sheer discipline of the studio and the tension between creativity and control acted as an imaginative release for the discovery of new processes. The dominating framework of relief blocks, intaglio plates, lithographic stones and silkscreens helped create unique avenues through which ideas were formed, developed and realised.

Artists' prints have always been a traditional part of art collecting and in common with other public art galleries, Cartwright Hall houses a substantial collection. Before the 1960s, the majority of the prints acquired were British and celebrated the portrait and landscape traditions of the 19th century. The

Frenchman Alphonse Legros (1837-1911) who taught printmaking in London at the Slade School for several years (and was made Professor of Etching in 1876), along with W R Sickert (1860-1942) James Whistler (1834-1903) and Francis Seymour Haden (1818 - 1910) were responsible for developing etching into one of the most widely used and exhibited of print mediums. Several of the intaglio prints in the Bradford collection reveal the galvanising effect that Legros had on this technique. A small group of vigorously etched landscapes, often including a lone figure, demonstrates the expressive qualities of the medium. The collection also includes good examples by Sickert himself, as well as Francis Seymour Hayden, Frank Short (1857-1943), Frank Brangwyn (1867-1956), William Lee-Hankey (1869-1952) and Therese Lessore (1884-1945).

In the 1960s, a few works were acquired to add a European dimension to the collection, including a small group of Old Master intaglio prints. These include the delicately engraved **Madonna and Child with Two Angels** by Albrecht Dürer (1471-1528) and the amusing **Virgil Suspended in a Basket** by Lucas van Leyden (1494-1533). Also purchased were etchings by Guido Reni (1575-1642), Juisepe Ribera (1591-1652), Salvator Rosa (1615-1673) and Dominico Tiepolo (1727-1804). Two magnificent late etchings by Francisco de Goya (1746-1828) from the terrifying **Disasters of War** series were acquired in 1977. The expressive black lines of the etching medium suited Goya's desolate mood perfectly, demonstrating that in a master's hands, small scale prints can have the same power as large scale works of art.

Also acquired in the same year were the **Illustrations to the Book of Job**, created by one of the masters of graphic media, William Blake (1757-1827), when he was in his sixties. These heroic engravings, together with his intimate wood-engraved illustrations to Virgil's **Ecologues**, exercised a powerful influence on at least two generations of British artists who were deeply impressed by Blake's breadth of vision and the passionate inner spirituality that he brought to his subject-matter. These artists and their successors chose to engrave their work on the end grain of wood, a relief technique long used by commercial printers for reproduction until discarded for newer technology. Fired by the intensity of Blake and inspired by the writings of John Ruskin and William Morris, small presses were established, producing from the late 19th to the early 20th century, immaculate wood engravings which could have the drama of hard contrast or the shimmer of a harmonious range of silvery tones. Other well-known prints in the collection come from the burins of Eric Gill (1822-1941), Blair Hughes-Stanton (1902-1981) and Edward Wadsworth (1889-1949). There are other equally impressive examples by Gertrude Hermes (1902-1983) and Gwen Raverat (1885-1957).

The colour relief prints of Japanese printmakers astonished European artists in the late 19th century. The influence that their shallow space and rhythmic sense of colour and design had upon the Impressionists is well recorded. The Japanese prints in the Cartwright Hall collection along with the ceremonial armour and beautifully carved netsuke and inro were acquired from two gentlemen travellers who had returned with these items along with other "exotic" objects from the Far East. Printed from the plank side of cherry, pear wood or sycamore, the works portray Kabuki actors, Sumo wrestlers, elaborately dressed courtesans and fierce warriors, in vibrant colours and arresting designs. Many of the prints are associated with the masters or apprentices of the schools of Hokkei (1780-1850), Hokusai (1790-1849), Hiroshige (1797-1850), Kunisada (1786-1864) and Kuniyoshi (1797-1864).

Nothing had prepared the 20th century for the social and artistic revolution that took place in the 1960s. An explosion occurred in printmaking as the traditional techniques of relief, intaglio and lithography were expanded to include the silkscreen process, hijacked from its commercial origins. Experimenting with the overt use of photography and mixed techniques, artists changed forever the notions of what actually made a picture and what constituted an original print.

Linked with the message that consumerism equals art anything could, and did, become an object worthy of picture making. Collaged objects were photo-screened or litho'd with the overall uniformity of a continuous surface. The English printmaker and writer Michael Rothenstein changed the concept of relief printing with his ingenious direct use of whole planks of wood with collage and additional photomechanical techniques. Under the leadership of American and British 'Pop' artists, photos became icons, and prints parodies of themselves. The lines between printmaking and painting became permanently smudged. In imitation of the billboard world of advertising, prints grew to enormous size. Flat areas of unmodulated colour echoed the anonymity of colour field painting in huge, markless screenprints. In America, new print workshops, such as Gemini in California, fed a market eager for experimentation; enthusiasm grew internationally.

In Bradford, the global print scene was monitored from the late sixties onwards by a major biennial exhibition, The British International Print Biennale. It was no accident that this exhibition was initiated at a time when printmaking had reached such an energetic high point. The general feeling that the Biennale initially democratised 'high' art was supported by the fact that, since a print was a multiple, people could now own an original, international work of art at an extremely reasonable price.

Following in the footsteps of other major print biennales in Yugoslavia, Norway and Poland, Bradford offered its enthusiastic visitors access to international art that covered a broad range of artistic and social issues. An advisory committee consisting of art experts, practitioners and administrators ensured that the most innovative and technically inventive artists participated in the exhibition. The eleven biennales organised between 1968-90 at Cartwright Hall included the works of artists such as the Americans Roy Lichtenstein and Andy Warhol, Gerd Winner and Arnulf Rainer from Germany and the South Africans Azariah Mbatha and Nils Burwitz. They exhibited alongside well-established and younger British printmakers such as Peter Blake, Tim Mara, John Walker, Ashley Cook and Amanda Faulkner. Art historians and contemporary art critics, thirsty for news of developments in Eastern Europe or in communist South-East Asia took advantage of the opportunity, unique in the UK, to view images direct from their creators. Through often circuitous routes, some artists escaped the control of their countries' cultural departments and showed work in Bradford which could not be exhibited in their own countries.

The contemporary print collections were purchased largely from these exhibitions. Invariably, many of the works were selected from countries with a strong printmaking tradition. Some link superb technical virtuosity with social or political comment, such as the deceptively academic yet ironic **Elite Cyclus Soldiers - Illusion and Reality** (1982) by the Czech artist Jiri Anderle or the robust **Violence in Town** (1979) by the Polish artist, Edward Dwurnik. Other printmakers, such as the German Georg Baselitz appeared to have turned away from the high tech methods so popular in the 1960s and 70s, stripping away technical gloss for a new graphic truth in simple but violently executed woodcuts such as **Bent Figure with Stick** (1984). The use of design and movement in the work of Azariah Mbatha and the Namibian John Muafangejo clearly comes from a highly developed artistic tradition, giving powerful integrity to their linocuts **Royal Wedding** and **South-West Africa** both of which were produced in 1982. The Turkish artist Ergin Inan, has created a delicate and witty drypoint, **Letter V** (1981) through the interplay between Western symbol and Eastern calligraphy.

A large collection of beautifully produced contemporary prints from Japan is a reminder that paper and print are still central to Japanese artistic thought. Often using technically ingenious methods, with a confident mix of media, works by Tetsuya Noda, Shoichi Ida and Susumu Endo, among others, form an extra-ordinarily cohesive group within the contemporary collections. Their work ranges from cool conceptualism and an objective form of surrealism to abstract works using breathtaking, delicate colour. The work demonstrates a complete understanding of the ways in which photomechanical techniques can be harnessed to the more traditional techniques of lithography and woodcut. We are made simultaneously aware of the richness of the past and the inventiveness of the present.

The prints of Bradford-born David Hockney occupy a key place in the collections which hold all of his best-known series of prints - **A Rake's Progress** (1961-63), **The Poems of C P Cavafy** (1966), **Six Fairy Tales From the Brothers Grimm** (1969) and **The Blue Guitar** (1977), as well as important single works. Whatever this inventive artist learns in one medium, he brings to another, so that his paintings, drawings, photographs and prints inform each other. The childlike world he illustrated in his Grimm's Fairy Tales allowed him to develop a pictorial, narrative language entirely in keeping with the subject matter. In so doing, he used a range of intaglio techniques to create the jaggedness of rocks or glass, or the soft aquatint effects of magical nights and hidden places.

Hockney sought out printers who had worked with Picasso in his late years, to assist him in producing twenty colour etchings for **The Blue Guitar**. This both extended his knowledge and heralded a shift in subject matter. Later in 1979, he was persuaded by another master printer, Ken Tyler, to work with coloured paper pulp. These crossed the borders between the unique and the multiple work of art. This resulted in a fresh treatment of a subject that had dominated his paintings of the 60s - swimming pools. It also dictated a move away from the control he had exercised over his drawings and prints into the looseness of Fauve-like expressionism. The diptych **Le Plongeur**, (1978) a result of this new direction, continues to be one of the most popular works in Cartwright Hall.

The glowing, blue-green of Howard Hodgkin's **David's Pool** (1985) alluded both to Hockney's interest in swimming pools and Hodgkin's own admiration for a fellow colourist. For Hodgkin and other British artist-printmakers, the use and manipulation of colour is a regular feature of their work. Patrick Caulfield, who was invited to design the poster for the Sixth British International Print Biennale, chose a vibrant, impenetrable backdrop of canary yellow, against which he set a slightly oriental vase of flowers in bold, unmodulated black with a flash of white. A subtler, more evocative feel for colour can be found in the prints of John Loker and Norman Stevens who, with the rock'n'roll enthusiast David Oxtoby, studied at the Bradford Regional College of Art with David Hockney.

In stark contrast to the sumptuousness of such colour works are the sombre, matter-of-fact lithographs and relief prints of Anthony Davies. His portraits of the communities of Northern Ireland make us aware that, whether in Derry or London's Brixton, poverty is a unifying factor. His work also serves as a reminder that from the time of Hogarth, prints have been powerful communicators of social messages. The use of earth, sky and water is a wider theme explored by many British printmakers - from the resonant grey/black aquatints of Norman Ackroyd's Yorkshire Moors to Julian Meredith's atmospheric fish prints.

Cartwright Hall's long association with printmaking continues through exhibition and acquisition. Recently works by Laila Rahman and Peter Howson have been acquired, the latter, a small group revealing the horror of civil war in Bosnia. They demonstrate with others in this rich and varied collection that printmaking is at its best when imagination and technique - however complex - combine to produce powerful, unforgettable images.

Caroline Krzesinska

Senior Keeper, Arts and Exhibitions

63

FRANCISCO GOYA (1746-1828)
The Carnivorous Vulture (from `The Disasters of War')
c. 1810-20
Etching 15 x 19.5 cm
Purchased with the assistance of the Victoria & Albert Museum
Purchase Grant Fund

YOSHI-IKU (1824-1895)
Sanada Yoshitada overcoming Matano Kagehisha
before a waterfall c.1850
Woodcut 35 x 24 cm
Presented by R.M.Priestman

MICHAEL ROTHENSTEIN (1908-1993)
New York 1974
Screenprint and relief print (edition
of 75) 65 x 53.5 cm
Commissioned for the Fourth British
International Print Biennale

ROY LICHTENSTEIN (born 1923)
Peace Through Chemistry 1970
Lithograph and Screenprint (edition of 32) 97 x 157.5 cm
© Roy Lichtenstein / DACS 1997

JIRI ANDERLE (born 1936)
Elite (Cyclus Soldiers - Illusion and Reality) 1982
Mixed media (edition of 70) 95.5 x 64 cm

EDWARD DWURNIK (born 1943)
Violence In Town 1978
Lithograph and collage (edition of 5) 69 x 49.5 cm

PATRICK CAULFIELD (born 1936)
Poster for the Sixth British International Print Biennale 1979
Screenprint (edition of 100) 84 x 59 cm
Commissioned for the Sixth British International Print Biennale

DAVID HOCKNEY (born 1937)
The Boy Hidden in a Fish
from The Little Sea Hare (Plate 4)
(from `Six Fairy Tales From The Brothers Grimm') 1969
Etching and aquatint (edition of 100) 23 x 27 cm
Purchased with the assistance of the Victoria & Albert Museum Purchase Grant Fund
© David Hockney

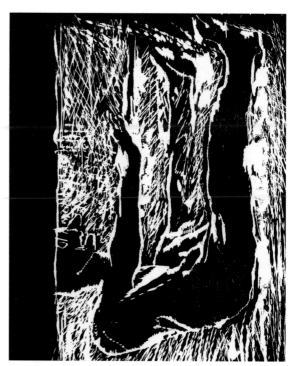

DAVID HOCKNEY (born 1937)
Figures With Still Life (from `The Blue Guitar')
Hard and soft ground etching with drypoint (edition of 200)
42.5 x 34.5 cm
Purchased with the assistance of the Victoria & Albert Museum
Purchase Grant Fund
© David Hockney

GEORG BASELITZ (born 1938)
Bent Figure with Stick 1984
Woodcut (edition of 12) 64.5 x 49.5 cm
Purchased with the assistance of the Victoria & Albert Museum
Purchase Grant Fund

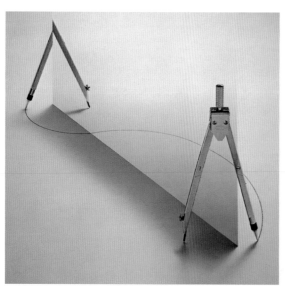

SUSUMU ENDO (born 1933)
Space & Space (Compasses) 1981
Lithograph (edition of 75) 45 x 45 cm

LAILA RAHMAN (born 1966)
The Worshippers Dance 1993
Etching and aquatint 40 x 39 cm

WILLIAM BLAKE (1757-1827)
Illustration to The Book of Job, plate 14
Engraving (Second edition) 1875 21 x 16 cm
Purchased with the assistance of the Victoria & Albert Museum
Purchase Grant Fund

ANTHONY DAVIES (born 1947)
Brixton / Derry, One Struggle 1981
Lithograph (edition of 16)
45 x 38 cm

Zoomorphic Horse
Iran late 18th or early 19th century
Ink, paint and gold leaf on paper 17 x 22.8 cm

SHAHZIA SIKANDER (born 1971)
Riding the Written 1993
Screenprint, pigment and tea wash on wasli 37 x 25.5 cm
*Purchased with assistance from the MGC / V&A Purchase
Grant Fund and the NACF*

Dastarkhan (Carpet on Floor cloth)
Machlipatnam 19th century
Blockprinted cotton 132 x 300 cm

Wall hanging
Turkey 19th century
Satin silk with gold, silver and silk thread embroidery 266 x 182 cm

Two Saris
Varanasi 19th century
Brocaded Silk   Navy and gold sari: 510 x 114.5 cm
                 Crimson and gold sari: 464 x 109 cm
Purchased with assistance from the MGC / V&A Purchase Grant Fund

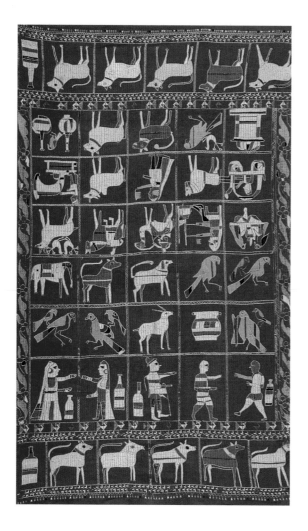

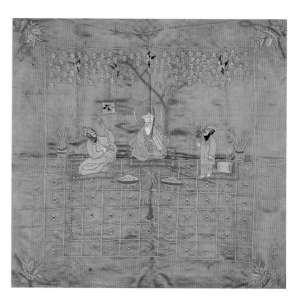

Textile with Guru Nanak and his two companions
Ahmedabad, Gujarat early 20th century
Silk with silk embroidery 68.5 x 73 cm
Presented by Cougar Freight Services

Phulkari
Punjab early 20th century
Cotton with floss silk embroidery 213.5 x 122 cm

NINA EDGE (born 1962)
Zero 1996
Batik on cotton 223 x 239 cm
*Funded from the proceeds of the National Lottery through the
Arts Council of England*

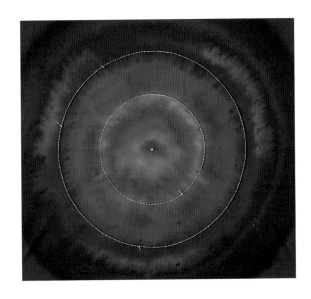

FAHMIDA SHAH (born 1966)
Untitled 1996
Silk with textile dyes and handpainting 209.5 x 112 cm
*Funded from the proceeds of the National Lottery through the
Arts Council of England*

SARBJIT NATT (born 1962)
Mughal 1996
Textile dyes and pigment on silk 168.5 x 110 cm
*Funded from the proceeds of the National Lottery through the
Arts Council of England*

Plaque depicting scene from the Ramayana
Karnataka early 19th century
Pierced gold 8.5 x 9.8 cm
Anonymous loan

Three talis (marriage pendants)
Tamil Nadu 19th century
Gold   Hanuman tali: 2 cm square
          Parvati and Shiva lingam tali: 2.2 x 0.8 cm
          Vishnu tali: 2 x 1.5 cm
Hanuman and Shiva talis funded by Friends of Bradford Art
Galleries and Museums

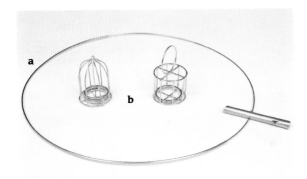

MAH RANA (born 1964)
a I Never Promised You a Rose Garden 1996
b His n' Hers 1996
Gold and steel   Pendant: 4.6 cm
                      Necklace circum: 61.2 cm
                      Domed cage: 3.4 x 8 cm
                      Drum cage: 4 x 7.6 cm
*Funded from the proceeds of the National Lottery through the
Arts Council of England*

Vishnu pendant
Himachal Pradesh, Central India
19th century
Cloissoné enamel on gold
3 x 2.5 cm

**Spiral Pendant from
Satavahana Period**
Deccan or Central India
1st century A.D
Gold wire with granulation
4.3 x 2.7 cm
*Presented by the National Art
Collections Fund*

Two Syrian Christian talis (marriage pendants)
Kerala early 20th century
a Gold with rubies: 3.5 x 2.5 cm
b Gold with applied gold decoration: 2.5 x 1.0 cm
Presented anonymously

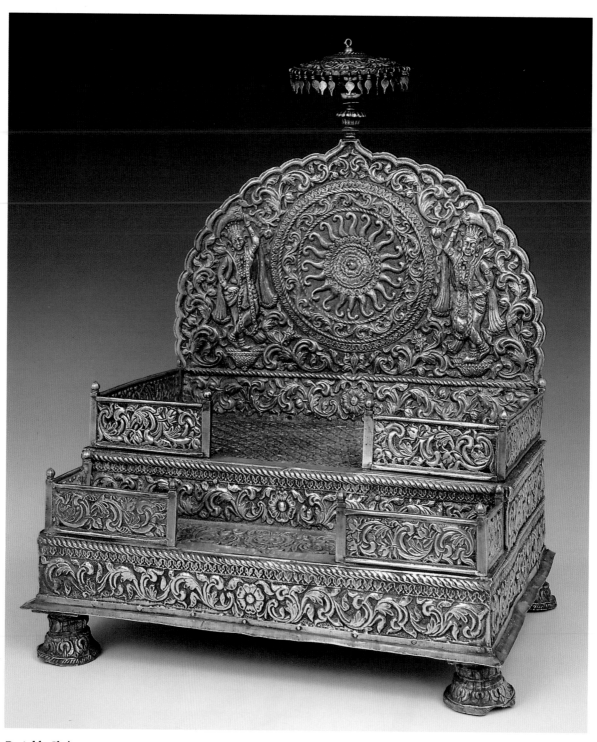

Portable Shrine
Rajasthan early 20th century
Silver 47 x 36.5 x 28 cm
Funded by the Friends of Bradford Art Galleries and Museums

Pandan (Betel leaf server)
Rajasthan early 20th century
Pierced silver 28.5 x 22.5 x 21 cm

Shank (Conch Shell)
Rajasthan early 20th century
Silver and shell 20 x 7 x 7 cm

Group of goldsmiths' moulds
Deccan and Himachal Pradesh late 19th - early 20th century
Brass and bronze   Family group   2 x 3.5 cm
                     Ganesh   4.5 x 4.5 cm
                     Fish   2 x 3.2 cm
                     Symbolic motifs   1.2 x 10.8 cm
                     Peacock   3.5 x 3.7 cm
                     Floral & plant motif 6.8 x 7.5 cm

Box, comb and rings
Partabgarh, Rajasthan 20th century
Gold on glass   box: 3.2 x 8.4 x 5.8 cm
                 comb: 11.3 x 3 x 0.9 cm
                 four rings each approximately:
                 2 x 1.6 x 2.2 cm

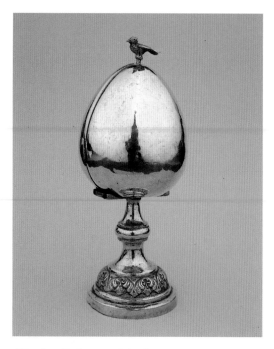

Attardan (Perfume container)
Rajasthan early 20th century
Silver with gilding   17 x 7.1 cm (closed width)
                             17 x 16.2 cm (open width)

a   b

Two cosmetic containers
South India early 20th century
Silver, gilt and turquoise   **a** 4.5 x 8.6 cm
                             b 8.2 x 11.2 cm

Parrot feeder
Gujarat early 20th century
Silver height: 26 cm, diameter: 28.5 cm

KALIM AFZAL (born 1966)
Fountain 1996
Glass   104 x 53.5 x 53.5 cm
Funded from the proceeds of the National Lottery through the
Arts Council of England

LORETTA BRAGANZA
Elemental Vessels 1996
Ceramic Slipware   40.8 x 36.3 x 7.5 cm
28.7 x 33 x 6.5 cm
16.6 x 21.8 x 5 cm
Funded from the proceeds of the National Lottery through
the Arts Council of England

HENRY PIM (born 1947)
Two vases 1984
Slab built stoneware 62 x 30 x 12 cm each
Presented by the Contemporary Art Society

PRISCILLA MORGAN-HILL (born 1965)
Three vessels 1996
Etched glass 29 x 56.5 cm
31.5 x 46 cm
30 x 54.5 cm
Funded from the proceeds of the National Lottery through the
Arts Council of England

KEYS TO THE MAGIC KINGDOM
THE NEW TRANSCULTURAL COLLECTIONS
OF BRADFORD ART GALLERIES AND MUSEUMS

Great pomp and ceremony attended the inaugural exhibition of Cartwright Hall Art Gallery in 1904. Launched by the then Prince and Princess of Wales, (later King George V and Queen Mary) the outlying Lister Park and the Hall itself became the venue for a series of festive events that drew all of the people of Bradford. One event much written about by the press of that time was the recreation of a Somali village in the grounds of the park. The Somalis attracted a great deal of attention and, judging from newspaper accounts, the curiosity was not unmixed with goodwill.

The reports also record moments of poignance and tragedy. A child was born to one of the Somali families and she was named Hadija Yorkshire. An inclement May hastened the death of one Somali woman who was found to have consumption. A large number of Bradford citizens turned out to mourn this sad event.

What makes the whole episode so shocking to us today was the study of living, breathing human-beings as though they were museum specimens or exotic animals in a zoo. It was, at best, an anthropological approach to the study of culture and very much of its time.

Today nearly a hundred years later, and indeed in Bradford's centenary year, the social composition of this Yorkshire city has changed beyond all recognition. A rapid process of expansion had, from the 1830s, converted it into an incipient landlocked entrepôt. Drawn by its growing prosperity, German merchants as well as shopkeepers and workers from Ireland, Scotland and Cumbria located themselves here. But it was the aftermath of the Second World War that witnessed the largest influx of settlers. Italians, Ukrainians, Poles and Pakistanis began to arrive, part of a vital process of rebuilding an enervated post-war Britain.

The manner of recording census statistics makes it difficult to place an exact figure on the number of East European residents in Bradford. But it would be safe to assume that the largest minority group in Bradford today is the South Asian community from the Indian sub-continent. Of a total population of 490,000 they comprise approximately 80,000. Although largely from Pakistan, there are also a number of people from India and Bangladesh as well.

The transcultural collections of Bradford Art Galleries and Museums are relatively new. Systematic purchasing was begun only in 1986 with an initial emphasis on contemporary art. Interestingly, the first donation to the Bradford Art Museum in 1879, presented by one of the sons of Titus Salt, was a suit of Japanese armour. An evolving acquisitions policy was commited to collecting in the broad areas of the Fine and Decorative Arts directly or indirectly related to the Indo-Pakistan sub-continent. A methodology was developed which guided the nature of the collecting. Temporary exhibitions were organised, usually as a result of community consultation. They covered a broad church, from themes as diverse as calligraphy, jewellery, manuscript paintings, textiles, and contemporary art.[1]

The audience response to these exhibitions served as valuable case-studies and informed the direction of the collections policy. It also became clear that there were certain categories of objects, which the initial policy had not particularly highlighted, that drew a deep emotional response from particular sections of the audience. At the same time these were also of great interest to the general public. This then was the touchstone that triggered buying within certain, hitherto unemphasised, areas. Calligraphy from the Muslim world, gold and silver, saris, costumes and ritual textiles are some examples. This meant that the original focus on contemporary South Asian art was widened in order to give the collection added depth and range. Bradford is fortunate in having minority communities from geographic areas or cultures rich in the material arts. However, the links between the holdings and the communities have been kept deliberately fluid.

These links have allowed us to collect objects whose aesthetic value is beyond question. There are a small number of objects in the collection that can be termed antiques, that were either donated or purchased within this country. But all the objects directly acquired from India or Pakistan are from the 1900s onwards. This is in compliance with the antiquity regulations of the two countries which forbid the export of artefacts over a hundred years old. This cut-off date has actually proved quite useful. It has demonstrated, beyond doubt, that the craftsmanship of the 20th century too can be of superlative quality. At the same time, the objects are also underpinned by the ethical imperative that they reflect, to a degree, the kaleidoscopic cultures of West Yorkshire making this the first non-colonial collection of its kind in the country.

There are, doubtless, other equally valid methodologies but this syncretistic approach appears to be the most appropriate one for Bradford. Commonwealth and post-colonial studies have been an area of burgeoning growth over the last twenty years, particularly in the field of literature and cultural studies. The critical discourse around this area include the writings of well-respected scholars such as Edward Said, Homi Bhabha and Gayatri Chakravorty Spivak. The decoding and deconstructing of various modes of thought such as Orientalism have been invaluable to a general understanding of structures of dominance and how these infiltrate and influence culture.

Many aspects of this discourse are valid and applicable to the Bradford collection, particularly the contemporary section. But this is essentially a long-term practical project and this essay, while reaffirming a deep respect for this discourse, temporarily sets it aside in order to let the public, the Bradford collections and the exhibitions develop their own momentum.

The establishment of a rolling programme of long-term display for the transcultural collection is part of a process of making it meaningful not only to our targeted audiences but to the general public as well. In addition to being aesthetically and ethically valid, the display has to be relevant. It needs to address a wide cross-section of the public while depicting the shifting, quicksilver nature of cultural pluralism.

The gallery in which the transcultural collections will be housed, is sited on the same floor as the Western permanent collections. The parity between the two arms of the collection is, therefore, stated without undue emphasis. It allows for the creation, in a manner that is not forced or contrived, of a variety of contexts that cross-reference between cultures. One approach adopted is that of juxtaposing apparently unconnected objects. Closer study will, however, reveal thematic, stylistic, historical or philosophical links. For instance, Laila Rahman's etchings will hang next to a selection of Blake's engravings from the **Book of Job** illustrating their shared humanistic and spiritual concerns.

Obviously, building up a collection from practically nothing can be an expensive business. Bradford has only had very modest resources. The Arts Council National Lottery, the M G C / V & A Purchase Grant Fund, the National Art Collections Fund and the Henry Moore Foundation have been invaluable in the generous financial support they have provided. Without their help there would not have been significant holdings.

The collections, at present, fall into four loose groupings:

1 **Contemporary Fine Arts and Crafts**

2 **Calligraphy from the Muslim World**

3 **Gold and Silver**

4 **Textiles**

CONTEMPORARY FINE ARTS AND CRAFTS

The category of contemporary arts and crafts overarches the other three categories of calligraphy, textiles, silver and gold. Indeed contemporary art makes frequent inroads into the three areas, since they too have a modern thrust. While they give it context, it gives them relevance. Contemporary art also operates as a sharp brake on any temptation to retreat into nostalgia. The primary focus of this collection is on artists of South Asian descent living and working in this country. This immediately poses a problem about the nature of definitions which was thrown into high relief by a recent event. In October 1996 Sotheby's of London held a major auction of **100 Years of Modern and Contemporary Indian Art**. Before the paintings went under the hammer, they were previewed at Cartwright Hall Art Gallery.

What was noticeable, about the list of selected artists, was that apart from Balraj Khanna, F N Souza and S H Raza (the post-war generation who had moved to Europe), all other artists lived and worked in India. Indeed, these three artists continued to have strong links with India while resident respectively in England, America and France. Sotheby's were defining, no doubt unwittingly, those artists that they perceived to be properly `Indian' or `Pakistani'. In so doing they had excluded the forty or more practising artists of Indo-Pakistan sub-continental descent living and working in Britain. This decision would have had nothing to do with their saleability or quality. For these artists included international names such as Anish Kapoor and Dhruva Mistry. Indeed, Kapoor sells faster than he can sculpt or draw.

Sotheby's, by articulating, however unselfconsciously, what they perceived to be genuinely Indian, had by exclusion, defined what they perceived to be non-Indian or indeed British. This is not without irony. Since the 1980's artists of South Asian descent have been locked in periodic conflict with the British art establishment over issues of marginalisation and interpretation. It was sixteen years ago, in 1981, when the race riots of Bristol, Birmingham, Liverpool and London galvanised the country and radicalised the thinking of a number of artists of non-British origin. Artists from the Indian sub-continent and the African and Caribbean countries had lived, struggled, modestly succeeded or failed long before then.

The turning point was 1981 when the work of these artists began to be treated almost as a movement, producing a body of work, with shared or overlapping concerns unique to their state of being non-European. The fact that most of them (with notable exceptions such as Rasheed Araeen) were relatively young, either second-generation Asians or fairly recent arrivals to Britain must have had a bearing. Artists such as Sutapa Biswas, Nina Edge, Chila Kumari Burman and Said Adrus combined both a public and private utterance in their work. Inevitably, one casualty of the attempt at homogenising `Black Art' was that public utterance, in the shape of social protest, alienation and anger, was often highlighted at the expense of the private utterance. To that extent the 80's was an uneasy age. The 90's signalled the beginning of a subtler and more introspective approach to the treatment and analysis of artists of dual heritage.

Contemporary artists practising in India and Pakistan today are very much part of the international art scene. Their work, while maintaining a distinct identity, has undoubtedly been shaped by 20th century

Western movements in art. Shanti Panchal and Dhruva Mistry who received their initial art training in India, but who have also lived and worked in Britain, are excellent examples of this composite training. But now the majority of the artists of South Asian descent have been trained in Britain and, therefore, almost exclusively in the Western tradition. They have had to 'discover' their Indian creative selves. Many of them illustrate what Homi Bhabha described as the state of being caught up in the space between frames.

".. double-lives are led in the postcolonial world, with its journeys of migration and its dwellings of the diasporic. These subjects of study require the experience of anxiety to be incorporated into the analytic construction of the object of critical attention: narratives of the borderline conditions of cultures and disciplines. For anxiety is the affective address of a world [that] reveals itself as caught up in the space between frames; a doubled frame or one that is split."[2]

For many of the artists, articulating this quest has involved the shadowy realm of speculation, dreams and the unconscious; the recollections of parents, family and childhood. These become instruments of 'knowing' a mixing of memory and desire, as once described by Sutapa Biswas in an unwitting echo of T S Eliot. The themes of displacement and quest, a search for identity, especially for those who no longer live in their country of origin, are firmly established in literature. The writings of V S Naipaul, for instance, explore this in dark and ambivalent detail. While this has been accepted as perfectly legitimate in literature, for some reason it is still slightly suspect in the visual arts and can be devalued as nostalgia, perhaps because it employs a visual vocabulary that is frequently unfamiliar to the West.

Nonetheless, the undertaking of this quest seems vital to the artists' creative well-being and often involves a series of journeys both metaphoric and real to the mother-country. For many of these artists, their academic, intellectual selves seem to be embodied by the West and their intuitive, instinctual selves by the Indian sub-continent. It is a composition that is equally male and female in its makeup. The metaphysical artist de Chirico (himself an Italian-Greek who had lived in Germany, France and Italy) believed implicitly in the theory that authentic modern art always had 'the element of surprise'. With these artists there is often the shock of the old; an atavistic memory or arcane knowledge that can surface in the most incredible of coincidences.

For instance, Biswas used a particular patterned fabric in **Housewives With Steak-Knives** (1985-86) in the garment for the Kali figure, the female principle, the destroyer and protective mother goddess (incidentally, the best-known and least understood Hindu deity). To Biswas's amazement she discovered later, on a visit to India, that the patterned fabric was identical to a cloth with the same eye/mouth motif used to ceremonially drape Kali images in Bengal.

Through the subtleties and nuances of such quests, artists of dual heritage feel they can find their true voice; one that has both integrity and dynamism. But this carefully worked out interior process is not often reflected in the audience response. There is frequently a reductionist reaction where the work is viewed in a way that is too rigidly culture-specific. The manner in which these artists are presented and interpreted, therefore, becomes crucial.

This is one of the reasons why this area is the most open-ended section of the Bradford collections. The edges are deliberately blurred to occasionally include the work not only of artists living and working in India, Pakistan and Bangladesh but also of Western artists. One of the most recent purchases is a work from Conrad Atkinson's **Landmine** series. Otherwise, the work of artists of dual heritage would be in danger of appearing decontextualised.

Bradford has, arguably, one of the most comprehensive collections of contemporary South Asian art in Britain today. It gives the collection its radical edge. It will also be of increasing historical importance, capturing as it does, a society in transition. Artists such as Nina Edge, Zarina Bhimji, Chila Kumari Burman and Saleem Arif depict notions of empowerment and reclaiming. They also restate their centrality within the British mainstream. Bradford has to be especially careful that the inclusion of artists from the disenfranchised Asian community, does not imply their exclusion from the British mainstream.

The collection spans a period of approximately sixty years, from the 1930s to the present day. The earliest work is by, one of India's great moderns, the enigmatic Amrita Sher-Gil (1913-1941), who died tragically young at the age of twenty-eight. The collection itself was launched in 1986 with the purchase of fifteen works by Jamini Roy (1887-1972) another of India's important modern artists. Balraj Khanna, Bhupen Khakhar, Anish Kapoor, Dhruva Mistry, Arpana Caur, and Salima Hashmi are some of the other notable names also represented.

The collection was given added powerful momentum with the award of an Arts Council Lottery grant in 1995. This enabled Bradford to commission works from over thirty artists and makers such as Perminder Kaur, Zarina Bhimji and Avtarjeet Dhanjal. The collection, on the whole, embodies a variety of narratives and concerns. It also reveals an impressive breadth and range of talent.

The works produced by a number of 'makers' as opposed to 'artists' such as Mah Rana, Lubna Chowdhary, Nina Edge, Loretta Braganza, Sarbjit Natt and Fahmida Shah patently demonstrate the absurdity of the hierarchical demarcation between the Fine Arts and Crafts. Rana, Chowdhary and Braganza's works could as easily be termed small sculpture, albeit in gold and ceramics. Edge, Natt and Shah are essentially artists who tend to work on textile rather than canvas.

Many of the commissioned artists, recognising the importance of the interaction between the city, the people of Bradford and the collections have saluted the city in a number of ways. Chowdhary produced a series of nine architectural landmarks entitled **Bradford City.** Using stoneware clay she has successfully reproduced the warm tones of the creamy-beige of Bradford stone. Cartwright Hall, City Hall and Listers Mill are some of the buildings thus celebrated.

The pieces are extraordinary in terms of the firing technique alone. Far more representational than her usual body of work, of which Bradford also has several examples, these buildings have the exquisite detailing of ivory. They are deliberately not to scale which confers on them a child-like honesty. This is further enhanced by the fact that they are stood on amusing little feet. The glass maker Kalim Afzal, who was brought up and educated in Bradford, has created a ruby-streaked amethyst glass fountain straight out of the Arabian Nights.

Bhajan Hunjan used motifs and objects from the silver collection for her work **One and Many**. Unusually, sixteen sections of canvas are contained within one frame. Sunburst motifs, hookahs, receptacles for holy Ganges water, vermilion powder and opium emerge in ghostly, bleached relief like photographic negatives, against a golden yellow background. The squares are unified by a faintly discernible circle and the jali motif (pierced arabesque and geometric patterns used in architecture in wood, stone or marble).

Hunjan is not the only artist to interpret the traditional landscape or portrait format of a canvas differently. Pushing the frontiers, metaphorically speaking, sometimes seems to involve questioning the structure and shape of the material on which artists imprint their statements. Saleem Arif's painting **The Vessel of Vitality** is literally carved in the shape of a bowl, brimming with oceanic waters. A cut-out fish shape allows the usually anonymous background wall to become part of the installation. Said Adrus's **Portrait of Another Kind** is an asymmetrical diptych hung vertically. One is led to examine issues of identity and appearance, and their physical and causal links, in this work. A xeroxed copy of the first page of a British passport with the crown and herald is a central image. The passport states where you have the right to live, but it cannot tell you who you really are. Appearance, on the other hand, cannot fix nationality. The person in the portrait is suggested, rather than represented, by objects belonging to him or her - a pair of spectacles and blue jeans.

Perhaps one of the most profound works to emerge from the commissioning process is Salima Hashmi's pictographic map of the Indo-Pakistan sub-continent entitled **Zones of Dreams.** The map, although accurate in its locations, has a mythic presence. Hashmi presents the sub-continent as a geographic entity, a vast landmass hemmed in by oceanic waters on three sides and bordered by the majestic Himalayan mountain range on the fourth. Flashes of history, myth, fable and dream irradiate the magical realms. Wondrous fish and an Iranian simurgh or phoenix move in the seas. Sri Lanka, described as a gem about to surface from the ocean in an ancient Indian text, is submerged in emerald waters. Bangladesh, too often portrayed as hapless victim to the furies of nature, is symbolised by sprays of lotus blossom, in memory of a land that was celebrated in poetry and song as beauteous and plentiful.

The map is like a palimpsest, simultaneously occupying different time-frames, with faint traces of history, fleeting man-made marks, echoes of past triumphs, tragedies and fragments of ancient text. A column of kalamkari motifs to the right refers to the indirect, pre-colonial textile trade between India and other regions including the West. Agra, the location of the fabulous Taj Mahal is marked with a barely discernible jali pattern, while Lucknow has a delicate paisley in celebration of the "white on white" chikan kari embroidery for which the region is famed.

In Hashmi's own words "I wanted the work to reinforce the romance associated with maps - the unfolding of the mysteries associated with travel and discovery. I drew upon my own memories of different cartographic traditions as well as childhood stories, tourist trivia and contemporary imagery. I wanted to knit together references from court and religious manuscripts, folk cultures and well-known visual clichés."

But although Kashmir slumbers discreetly under a blanket of snow the dogs of war can still be heard. A nervous ominousness pervades as clouds billow across the horizon, hinting at a social and political turbulence that threaten to overwhelm entire regions. **Zones of Dreams** is haunted by a sense of precarious balance and imminent danger.

Placed in the introductory passage to the gallery, **Zones of Dreams** heralds the entry into a strange and rich magic kingdom. Separated by a pilaster and moving from the macrocosm to the microcosm are views of Bradford by David Hockney and Francis Newton Souza. The map and the Bradford views are visual and symbolic articulations of the journey from the Indo-Pakistan sub-continent to Bradford that so many Asians in the city undertook.

The actual entrance to the gallery itself is, appropriately enough, flanked by two of Dhruva Mistry's eponymous bronze guardian figures **Guardian I** and **Guardian II**. These part-animal, part-human figures mediate an entry into a different yet familiar world.

CALLIGRAPHY FROM THE MUSLIM WORLD

"When its parts are symmetrical, its alif and its lam made long, its lines regular, its terminals made similar to its upstrokes, its 'ayns opened, its ra clearly distinguishable from its nun, its paper polished, its ink sufficiently black, with no commixture of styles, permitting of rapid visualisation of outline and quick comprehension of content, its separations clearly defined, its thinness and thickness in due proportion... It should disregard the style of the copyists and avoid the artistry of the elegant writers, and it should give you the suggestion of motion, though stationary".

IBN MUQLAH ON CALLIGRAPHY, 9th CENTURY A.D.

Although most cultures value good handwriting, it is not as central to other religious and aesthetic sensibilities as it is to Islam. The Chinese and the Japanese have a highly evolved calligraphic tradition, but in sheer ubiquity and range of materials used, they appear to be outstripped by countries where Muslim culture flourishes. The reasons for the seemingly exaggerated importance given to this art are numerous. The use of the Arabic script throughout most of the Muslim world helped forge a distinct and powerful Islamic identity, further reinforced by a widespread disapproval of depictions of the human form. Turkey, where Arabic was officially replaced by English in 1928 by Ataturk, and Bangladesh where Bengali is used, are perhaps the only two major Islamic countries that do not use the Arabic script.

Calligraphy is also revered because it is the instrument through which the Quran, the teachings of Allah as revealed to his Messenger the Prophet Mohammed (571-632 AD) was recorded. The divine revelation had to be couched in a script that was appropriately impressive and, consequently, form complemented content. In addition to this, there was the intrinsic beauty of the Arabic script itself, with its fluid and undulating lines.

Arabic, which is written from right to left, has 28 consonantal letters to the alphabet, long and short vowels being indicated by dots and brief strokes above and below the letters. The immense elasticity and flexibility of the script, where letters can extend into infinity or be compressed to a minute speck, lent itself to a wide variety of media outside the traditional papyrus, parchment, vellum, and, after the 8th century, paper.

Calligraphy was used on stone and marble monuments, incised on gemstones like carnelian, inscribed on gold, silver and other metals, woven, printed or embroidered onto textiles, carved on wood or painted onto ceramics. The floral, entwined, arabesque and geometric patterns that characterise so much of the art in the Muslim world, were the perfect foil for Arabic calligraphy, either incorporating it into the main design or embellishing it. Completely in keeping with the holistic nature of Islam, where the sacred and the secular sustain each other, calligraphy was firmly linked with various developments within Muslim culture, its art (both figurative and non-figurative), its sciences and its mystic tradition.

A good calligrapher, at his or her peak, achieved a concentration that was almost mystical. This was particularly true when writing the name of Allah or the Basmala "In the Name of Allah, the Merciful, the

Compassionate". (The Basmala is more popularly referred to as the Bismillah. Refer to Glossary). Inevitably `Allah' the `Basmala' and `al Asma` al Husna' (the 99 most beautiful names of Allah) were thought to have a protective, talismanic power in themselves. There developed a sub-culture of magical lore within Muslim cultures, where calligraphic amulets and charms were linked to numerology and astrology and were believed to have occult qualities. This was generally disapproved of by Muslim orthodoxy, but ultimately calligraphy is so entwined with the core of Muslim thought and teaching, that it is assured continuity in spite of changing fads and fashions.

The small Bradford collection of calligraphy from the Muslim world was started in 1990 as a response to the enthusiasm generated by an exhibition on **Islamic Calligraphy** in 1987. Although the emphasis has been on calligraphy from the Indo-Pakistan sub-continent, the collection, as it continues to grow, is intended to be pan-Islamic and includes items from Syria, Turkey, Iran and Egypt. To reflect the versatile nature of this art-form, the collection covers a range of media-textiles, gemstones, silver, bronze, brass, wood and paper.

The calligrapher working within this seemingly circumscribed art-form, where creativity is often further fuelled by devotion, often manages to produce work of great liveliness, ingenuity and variety. The life and movement conveyed by a 19th century zoomorphic horse from Iran demonstrates this perfectly. A pair of 19th century walnut chairs from Syria are conceived as much as pieces of sculpture as furniture. The imagination unleashed whether in the perfect, minutely inscribed, luminous carnelians from Deccani India or in the dramatic ivory, green and gold 19th century Turkish wall hanging can be both bold and conceptual.

This collection, however, is meant to be a living one. Contemporary artists from Muslim cultures use calligraphy in a far more radical or modernist manner than did their forbears. Calligraphy in the hands of a distinguished artist like Shirazeh Houshiary, becomes a tool for detachment, transcendence and the expression of alienation as revealed in **What I tell about me I tell about you**, a piece inspired by the Sufi poetry of Rumi. The endlessly repeated alphabetic characters in graphite on paper are as much gestural mark making or yantric forms as calligraphy. The work can be read in oppositional ways, the notations, coiled upon themselves, seem either to be drawn by an irresistible centripetal pull towards the nebular vortex or to spiral with centrifugal force away from the vortex.

Shahzia Sikander uses calligraphy in fractured forms in **Riding the Written** where ornate script metamorphoses into truncated horses symbolising historical events of disjunction and chaos. Both artists would emphatically not see themselves as calligraphers and would perhaps fit more comfortably within the category of contemporary art in the collection. Nonetheless, their works clearly indicate that calligraphy can still be used in unexpected ways today to plumb unsuspected depths.

GOLD AND SILVER

In 1988, in collaboration with the Victoria and Albert Museum, an exhibition of Indian jewellery was organised at Cartwright Hall. **A Golden Treasury: Jewellery from the Indian sub-continent** drew large audiences and it was obvious that as with **Islamic Calligraphy** gold and silver touched a deep cord within particular communities.

For Hindus, especially, gold has mystical connotations. Lakshmi, the goddess of wealth is supposed to dwell in gold. This accounts for the taboo among a large number of Hindus about wearing gold below the hip, since having one's legs or feet touch Lakshmi is disrespectful. Gold has always exercised a mysterious influence on the human mind throughout the world. A metal whose main functional use is ornamentation depends on the peculiarities of human psychology for its continuing power. The Indian sub-continent is reportedly the largest single repository of privately owned gold. It is not just the quantity of gold held that is so impressive, it is also the quality and range of the craftsmanship. Temple and other ritual, talismanic and marriage jewellery offer some of the best examples of the goldsmith's marvellous artistry.

Indian sculpture from Bharhut, Sanchi and Amaravati, for instance, dating approximately from the 2nd century B.C. to the 3rd century A.D. gives a clear idea of the extravagance and splendour of early Indian jewellery. Indeed, this is true of later Indian sculpture as well. Even today, the design vocabulary of the gold and silversmiths is rich and complex. They appear to draw from a lexicon similar to that of the textile weaver and the surface decorator. Again, as with textiles, there are an immense number of regional styles. Indian jewellery can be sculptural, architectural, abstract, organic or geometric in form. The deities of the Hindu pantheon, sacred birds and beasts, mystic symbols and the fruit, flowers and other vegetal forms of the natural world are just a few examples of the motifs used in gold and silver. Lapidary skills are also of a high standard and often semi-precious stones are themselves carved into figurative and floral forms.

The relatively unchanged nature of the design, allowing for the vagaries of fashion, is fortuitous. There are long gaps in the chronology of jewellery because, as an easily realisable asset, gold tends to be melted down. The comparitive purity of Indian gold, which is usually 22 carat, also means that the gold retains its value. Gold probably commands the highest price in India since demand frequently outstrips supply. The modern goldsmith has consequently learned to craft jewellery out of impossibly small quantites of metal. Yet temple endowments in gold can be on a staggeringly lavish scale. The gold temple chariots of Udipi in South Canara are a case in point.

The gold collection of Bradford Art Galleries and Museums is still at an evolving rather than a realised stage. Two notable new additions are a gold spiral pendant attributed to the Satavahana period (1st B.C.-3rd century AD) gifted to Bradford by the National Art Collections Fund and an unusual 19th century enamelled pendant of Vishnu from Himachal Pradesh. A beautiful gold plaque depicting a scene from the **Ramayana** from Karnataka is on long-term loan from a private lender. The granulation, enamelling and pierced work technique employed, in these three pieces, is quite superb.

Other items in the collection include a navratna (nine gem) pendant or a celestial talisman from Rajasthan. The nine gems, when arranged in a certain order, are meant to represent the nine planets. Navratna is popular throughout India, in the form of pendants, rings or entire suites. The collection also includes filigreed jewellery and talis or South Indian marriage pendants. These small gold lozenges have images and symbols of various gods from the Hindu pantheon such as Vishnu, Shiva and Parvati. The London-based contemporary jeweller Mah Rana, when commissioned to produce jewellery for Bradford took the marriage pendants as her source of thematic inspiration. The result were two sardonically witty pieces, a pendant gold stem with sharp thorns entitled **I Never Promised You A Rose Garden** and two gold rings encased in fragile, pretty gold cages made from secondhand melted down wedding rings called **His 'n' Hers**.

The collection also includes gold on glass work from Partabgarh. In the 19th century, the towns of Partabgarh in Southern Rajasthan and Indore and Rutlam in Madhya Pradesh were well known for their method of producing jewellery of chased gold on coloured glass. The goldsmiths made ornaments of plaques of glass with gold and silver ornamentation. Very thin perforated sheet gold in a variety of figurative and floral shapes are hammered out on blocks of resin and then fused with a blowpipe onto sheets of coloured glass usually taken from windows of defunct palaces. This particular glass seems to have been imported from Europe. Earlier examples use much thinner glass, which is almost invariably green in colour. Several branches of one family in Partabgarh are involved with this secret craft which has had a recent revival although it never completely died out. The motifs are taken equally from Hindu mythology or from Mughal courtly hunting scenes.[3] The skill required, for instance, to produce the extremely fine detailing of the peacock on the lid of one of the artefacts in the collection gives an indication of the talent of these goldsmiths.

An interesting adjunct to the gold is a collection of approximately 30 goldsmiths' moulds with a variety of human, animal, bird, fish and other symbolic motifs deeply engraved onto a cast bronze-type metal. These lovely little moulds are works of art in their own right. They allow numerous replicas of an image to be produced by hammering sheet gold or silver into these existing shapes.

Silver, poetically called chandi, is a popular semi-precious metal. Because it is less expensive than gold, the craftsmen have felt free to be more experimental. Pieces can be massive and boldly executed and cover a much wider range of domestic artefacts. The Bradford collection, which is almost exclusively early 20th century and comes mainly from Gujarat and Rajasthan, falls into two categories, ritual and secular silver. What characterises the silver is the minimal technology utilised, coupled with an extraordinarily skilled craftsmanship. The mobile shrine is an extremely complex construction, nevertheless, no heat has been used in its production.

The nature and function of the secular pieces provide interesting insights into the manners and customs of a more traditional and leisurely way of life for the prosperous classes in the past. The very names of the objects have a musical cadence, attardan, doopdan, surmadan, sindurdan, pandan, surahis and gulabpash. The more prosiac English translations read as perfume, incense, kohl, vermilion and betel leaf containers, water or wine flagons and rose-water sprinklers.

The **Kama Sutra** of Vatsyayana is usually too narrowly viewed as a manual for erotic instruction. It is also a minutely detailed documentary on social codes of dress and behaviour in order to live life at a sensuous, pleasurable and cultured level. A great deal of attention was paid to sringar or personal adornment and toilette by both men and women. (Sringar also refers to love and eroticism). In the chapter on "The life of a Citizen" the householder is enjoined to:

wash his teeth, apply a limited quantity of ointments and perfumes to his body, put some ornaments on his person and collyrium on his eyelids and below his eyes, colour his lips and look at himself in the glass. Having then eaten betel leaves and oher things to give fragrance to the mouth...He should bathe daily, [and] anoint his body with oil every other day [4]

The silver described earlier would obviously have been the perfect accoutrement for the process of sringar. They are not objets de luxe for they all had a demonstrable practical use. Sringar in art is often depicted in the form of a woman looking into a mirror. Fittingly the collection includes a beautifully patterned silver vanity box with a mirror within.

The ritual silver includes an elaborately repousse-work mobile silver shrine, mentioned earlier, and other paraphernalia meant for puja or worship such as lamps, bell, conch shell and panch patra (vessels for the sacramental five foods of yoghurt, honey, milk, ghee and sugar). Even the sacred objects have a personal, domestic quality to them as pujas are conducted in both the temple and the home. The lighting of the lamps, the ringing of the bell, the wafting of incense, the ritual ablution of the gods using the conch shell, and the sharing of the sacramental foods, conjure up a section of society at ease with itself. A pair of silver horn covers and an elaborate bird feeder complete a picture of a privileged class who appeared to have lived life to the full.

TEXTILES

For thousands of years Indian textiles, particularly muslins and cottons, were a major source of revenue for the sub-continent. The processes of spinning, dyeing and weaving had obviously been perfected to a high art. Pliny the Elder (23-79 AD) complained that the importing of muslins, or 'woven webs of wind' so popular in the Rome of his time, seriously depleted the city's coffers.

Indian myths often use weaving as a metaphor for the creation of the universe. The sutra or spun thread was the foundation, while the sutradhara or holder of the thread was the architect or creator of the universe.

For several hundreds of years, India's chief export had been textiles. When the East India Company was established, on the last day of the year 1600, regional Indian ports had an established trade in textiles with various countries in Asia, using traditional sea-routes. In fact, the British themselves initially bought Indian textiles, paid for in silver bullion. The British bartered most of these textiles for spices and pepper from Indonesia. Indonesia had been a buyer of Indian textiles, particularly the prized ikats of Gujarat since medieval times. With the expansion of British power in India the mechanised technology of the Industrial Revolution meant that textiles could be produced far more quickly and cheaply, albeit with a loss of quality. By 1911, so completely were the roles of buyer and seller reversed that India now bought ten percent of Britain's exports, more than any other country in the world. The main import was cotton piece goods. Yet for a long time Indian textiles were still the standard against which British textiles were measured. There was a concerted attempt to equal or surpass, through the machine-made muslins of Europe, the legendary muslins of Dacca.

Gandhi launched the swadeshi movement during the struggle for Indian Independence. Indians were successfully exhorted to boycott foreign goods, particularly textiles. After independence in 1947, Weavers' Service Centres were set up in key textile capitals all over India. They guarantee weavers a certain amount of commissioned work and supply them with equipment and designs. Surprisingly, such official support has not had a totally stultifying effect on the creativity of the textile craftsmen. However, survival for the average weaver can still be a desperate and precarious business.

The Bradford collections demonstrate the weaving and surface decoration techniques in which the Indian textile worker excels and which keep millions of them in work. Brocades, ikats, tie-dyes, block prints and embroidered textiles are some of the areas represented. The embroidered dowry textiles of Gujarat and Rajasthan, the phulkaris, produced mainly by Sikh women of Eastern Punjab, and saris from all over India are three of the main areas within this collection.

A particularly rare example of mochi embroidery from Gujarat is an early 20th century silk panel showing Guru Nanak (1469-1539) founder of Sikhism, with his two companions Bala and Mardana. Mochis, who are from the cobbler community, created wonderful embroideries by using the chain and satin stitch to delicate effect. They tended to use the cobbler's awl rather than a needle, which enabled them to produce much finer embroidery. This panel must have been commissioned by one of the members of the small Sikh community based in Ahmedabad in Gujarat.

The embroidery tradition of phulkaris (flowering work) and baghs (gardens) is a domestic art practised with a degree of sophistication by the women of Punjab. The date of its origin is unclear since early literature and records kept of brides' trousseaux make no mention of it. It flourished, particularly, in the 19th and early 20th century. The Bradford collection consists of textiles done exclusively by Sikh embroiderers although Hindus and Muslims also practised this art. Phulkari is embroidery in which the, usually, earth-coloured, coarse, homespun background material is clearly visible through the stitches. The pattern is formed through an ingenious combination of thread and material. Bagh, which is a more elaborate form of phulkari, is completely covered in embroidery so that the background cloth is not visible. The embroidery appears to be the woven cloth itself.

The main stitches used are the long and short darn stitch over counted threads using untwisted floss silk. No pattern or drawing was used and the motifs are usually stylised or geometric. The women interpreted the world around them, often with intelligent humour. Peacocks, parrots, ears of wheat and barley, doorways to Gurdwaras or Sikh temples, gold coins and jewellery were some of the most common motifs used. The train, an object of great fascination to the printmaker as well, was another popular motif although the Bradord collection does not, as yet, include an example of this, but it has an image of a horn gramophone.

The Bradford sari collection which, apart from five 19th century brocades, were all woven in the early 1990s is proof that the Indian textile worker can still produce the most exquisite of textiles. A classic costume, of standardised size, in high fashion for nearly 2,000 years, sounds inconceivable. However, in the case of the "unstitched but highly structured"[5] sari, as Jyotindra Jain described it, it is true. The continued popularity of the sari as an every day as well as a fashion garment provides those superb master craftsmen of India, the textile workers, with a definite and continuing source of patronage in an otherwise fickle world.

Most of the saris in the collection are a marvel of technique and design. Perhaps one of the most unusual is an Orissa ikat with a coded love poem woven onto the ground cloth. No mean feat when the intricate, labour intensive nature of ikat weaving is taken into consideration. Sections of the warp or weft threads are resist dyed to a programmed pattern. With double-ikats sections of *both* the warp and weft threads are resist-dyed. When woven the patterning on the warp and weft mesh to produce complex designs.

The colour palette of the saris needs particular mention since it is subtle, rich and sublime. It ranges from the palest ivory and mist to shimmering rose golds, amethyst, ruby, sapphire and emerald shades. They can be as changeable as the ocean and the sky.

Textile artists from Britain are an important part of this collection and inject an individual rather than collective creativity into the works. Fahmida Shah's sumptuous hand-painted silk is influenced by the sculptural architecture of Cartwright Hall, although abstracted out of all recognition. There is an element of light-heartedness with the introduction of mask-like faces inspired by an exhibition on heavy metal - **Sound and Fury** at Cartwright Hall in 1995. Shah was fascinated by the contrast - the fluid nature of a very contemporary theme with Harley Davidson motorbikes and neo-gothic art balanced by the solidity of the traditional architecture.

Natt's textile, **Mughal**, operates as a counterbalance. Formal rows of Mughal architectural shapes above and below a band of jade green skyline, immediately recall the pageantry of that glorious and oppressive world when art and architecture enjoyed a troubled golden age.

Nina Edge's batik textile entitled **Zero**, on the other hand, is an extremely subtle, understated, philosophical piece. Shades of indigo blue are punctuated by a slightly irregular circle of dots, some of which are shot through by spermatozoa-like shapes. This circle surrounds a minute white central disc. The piece reflects on the nature and depiction of zero in acknowledgement of the Indian thinkers who had refined this concept by the 6th century AD. Zero had many names and many symbols including the dot before it arrived at the shape as we now know it. Zero embraces infinity, it is nothing and it is everything, and this is what Edge celebrates in this work.

The collection includes other objects as well, works in ceramic, glass, wood, stone and metalware. Although there are notable pieces in each category, they are still small in number, and need augmentation to make them significant.

This seemingly disparate grouping is united by a common cultural heritage, (although interpreted very differently by different artists), aesthetic quality and the collective needs, primarily, of the Bradford public. It will be displayed in a gallery without a name, in line with other numbered but unnamed galleries on the same floor, and is dedicated to the people of Bradford, the craftsmen of the Indo-Pakistan sub-continent and all the artists of this country.

Nima Poovaya-Smith

Senior Keeper, International Arts

1 Islamic Calligraphy (1987) **A Golden Treasury: Jewellery from the Indian sub-continent** (1988), **Earthen Shades: The Paintings of Shanti Panchal** (1989), **Manuscript Paintings from the Ramayana** (1989), **Warm and Rich and Fearless: An Exhibition of Sikh Art** (1991), **101 Saris from India** (1992), **Living Wood: South Indian Sculpture** (1992), **Worlds Beyond: Death and the Afterlife in Art** (1993) and **An Intelligent Rebellion: Women Artists of Pakistan** (1994).

2 Bhabha, Homi, K.1994. **The Location of Culture.** "How Newness enters the world" p 213-214, London:Routledge.

3 I am indebted to Robert Skelton for information on the gold and glass work of Partabgarh which he was given the privilege to observe at first-hand.

4 Vatsyayana, circa 1st - 6th century A.D. **The Kama Sutra,** (trans. Richard Burton and F.F. Arbuthnot) (1995 ed.) p.30, Hertfordshire:Wordsworth Editions.

5 Jain, Jyotindra, 1982. **The Master Weavers.** "Introductory Notes on Indian Textiles" p. 114, Delhi: Festival of India publication.

CATALOGUE

For two-dimensional pieces, height precedes width.

For three-dimensional pieces, maximum sizes have been used.

PAINTINGS

SALEEM ARIF (born 1949)

Vessel of Vitality 1994

Oil on muslin and wood 110 x 160 cm

Purchased in 1996 and funded from the proceeds of the
National Lottery through the Arts Council of England

F1996.7

"In the East it is all pattern, whereas in the West it is all shadow" Arif once said. **Vessel of Vitality**, like most of his recent work, mediates between pattern and shadow. The curved shapes challenge the conventional rectangles and squares of Western painting. The fish-shaped sculpted aperture, in this painting, forces the normally anonymous background wall to our attention. The paint is applied in thick, immaculate, controlled layers. In many ways his works are as much sculpture as painting. The colours invariably have symbolic meaning. Blue, in **Vessel of Vitality** for instance, represents the sea and air and is also the colour of contemplation. The fish is a favourite emblem, as is the bird; their ability to move in elements other than earth obviously imbues them with almost magical properties. Arif was born in Hyderabad, India and came to Britain when he was 16 years old.

NPS

SYLVAT AZIZ (born 1954)

Exodus Lahore 1993

Pigment, woodcut, silver foil, dye, henna, etched prints, collage, ink and rhoplex on cotton paper 122 x 236 cm

Purchased in 1995 with support from the V&A/MGC Purchase
Grant Fund and the National Art Collections Fund

F1995.18

Exodus Lahore is a triptych with a busy, seemingly playful plethora of figures and script. The city of Lahore has thirteen gates or darwazas which, over the centuries, have been points of entry, invasion and, during the partition of 1947, flight. This is chronicled in this extraordinary work. **Exodus Lahore** is in warm parchment colours using

organic materials like henna. The cheerful colours are belied by violence and destruction. People are being decapitated by sword-wielding horseman. The chaos of invasion and flight are formally contained within the famous Lahore gates. The uppermost border comprises a stylised row of flames that threatens to engulf the city. Recreating the format of old maps, Aziz shows the tragic consequences of their drawing and redrawing. The middle panel has an inset image of a Brahmin priest - a reminder that pre-partition Lahore included Hindus and Sikhs. Aziz trained in Pakistan and now lives in Canada.

NPS

WRIGHT BARKER (1863-1941)

Circe c.1889

Oil on canvas 138 x 199.5 cm

Presented bY W. H. North in 1902

1902-3

Greek mythology was an important source of subject matter for Victorian artists. In this episode from Homer's *Odyssey*, the sorceress Circe is seen welcoming Odysseus and his shipmates to her palace. She fell in love with Odysseus and tried to persuade him to stay with her, drugging his companions and then turning them into swine.

Barker was a Bradford artist, well known as a painter of farm animals. Here, he turns his hand to higher themes, using his skill on wolves and lions, the warmth of their fur and the redness of the poppies contrasting with the cold marble stairs. Barker exhibited regularly at the Royal Academy until 1904. He ended his career as an art dealer in Harrogate.

CAH

SUTAPA BISWAS (born 1962)

Housewives With Steak-Knives 1985-86

Pastel, acrylic and xerox collage on paper mounted on canvas   274 x 244 cm

Purchased in 1994 with the assistance of the MGC/V&A Purchase Grant Fund

F1994-11

Housewives With Steak-Knives in many ways symbolises the radical aspect of British art in the 1980s, particularly by non-white artists, discovering various forms of empowerment. Painted when the artist was still a student at the University of Leeds it is one of her most reproduced works. **Housewives With Steak-Knives** is a self-portrait of the artist as the multi-armed Hindu Goddess Kali who is both protector and destroyer. Instead of the necklace of skulls, this image wears a necklace of portraits, the faces suggesting amongst others, Hitler and Trotsky. In one hand she holds a rose and collaged reproductions of **Judith and Holofernes** by the Renaissance artists Artemisia Gentileschi and Elisabetta Sirani. Another hand holds aloft a large steak knife. The range of erudite references both Western and Eastern in this work, challenges any attempt to confine it to 'ethnic' or 'black' art. Biswas was born in Santiniketan in West Bengal. Fittingly, it was here that the visionary poet-artist Rabindranath Tagore, set up his academy for the arts.

NPS

FORD MADOX BROWN (1821-1893)

The First Translation of the Bible into English: Wycliffe Reading his Translation of the New Testament to his Protector, John of Gaunt, Duke of Lancaster, in the Presence of Chaucer and Gower, his Retainers

1847-8, 1859-61

Oil on canvas 119.5 x 153.5 cm

Purchased in 1909

1909-52

A romanticised view of the Middle Ages inspired the artists associated with the Pre-Raphaelite Brotherhood. Ford Madox Brown here portrays an event from the 14th century, the scholar John Wycliffe reading to his patron, the Duke of Lancaster who sits with his wife and daughter. The poets Chaucer and Gower also listen attentively to the reading of the first translation of the Latin Bible into English. In 1859 the picture was 'improved' by Ford Madox Brown at the request of a new purchaser. The sky was brightened and a gold mount introduced to conceal the architectural surround. Madox Brown researched the historical details of his pictures meticulously, all details are authentically 'medieval'. Friends and family sat for the poses while the heads were based on prints or coins and medals.

Madox Brown was not actually a member of the Pre-Raphaelite Brotherhood which existed for only two years in the 1840s. Born and educated on the Continent, he travelled widely abroad.

CAH

FORD MADOX BROWN (1821-1893)

A small first sketch for "The First Translation of the Bible into English: Wycliffe Reading his Translation of the New Testament to his Protector, John of Gaunt, Duke of Lancaster, in the Presence of Chaucer and Gower, his Retainers" 1847

Oil on panel 18 x 25 cm

Purchased in 1980 with the assistance of the Victoria and Albert Museum Purchase Fund and the National Art Collections Fund

F1980-28

This is a small early study for the finished painting. Here, the paint is handled in a sketchy, looser manner and the original, more architectural surround inscribed with the names of the participants is still visible. The final version of the picture with its tableau-like quality has little visible evidence of brushstrokes.

CAH

ARPANA CAUR (born 1954)

The Embroiderer 1996

Oil on canvas 165 x 137.5 cm

Purchased in 1997 with funding from the proceeds of the National Lottery through the Arts Council of England

F1997-4

Arpana Caur lives in Delhi and is one of India's most acclaimed artists. Her recent works involve a direct interweaving of her own visual vocabulary with that of the ancient vocabulary of Mithila. The women of Mithila have painted, for hundreds of years, scenes drawn from Hindu religious epics. Mithila art continues to flourish even today. **The Embroiderer**, is like a creation myth painting, for the central figure could be weaving rather than embroidering. Her uplifted hand, as she embroiders, dominates the canvas. The embroiderer is nimbate, haloed by circle upon circle of Mithila-style bird-images. One bird-figure seems to emanate from her mouth, like a conch shell being blown at some ritual ceremony. The mythic stillness of the picture is counterbalanced by the tension of yet another halo of marching scissors, playful yet menacing.

NPS

GEORGE CLAUSEN (1852-1944)

The Boy and the Man c.1909

Oil on canvas 197.5 x 164 cm

Purchased from the artist in 1909

1909-19

The Boy and the Man has an element of symbolism, the upright figure of the boy taking time off to gaze into the distant future while the older man bends over his hoe, intent on his task. Clausen's technique here is interesting. Using a bright palette he has applied the paint when very dry, producing a heavily scumbled surface.

Clausen was born in London of Danish descent. He learned to paint at evening classes and worked for a time in the studio of the painter Edwin Long. He then studied at the Academie Julien in Paris where he saw the work of the French naturalist painter Jules Bastien-Lepage (1848-1884). He absorbed Bastien-Lepage's philosophy of painting out of doors (en plein air) combining it with the impressionist technique of Monet. Clausen was one of the most successful English painters of peasant life at the end of the century.

CAH

HON. JOHN COLLIER (1850-1934)

Queen Guinevere's Maying c.1897

Oil on canvas 180.5 x 121 cm

Presented by the daughters of the late William Rawlings J.P. in 1928

1928-1

The legends of King Arthur and his Knights of the Round Table had been revived by members of the Pre-Raphaelite Brotherhood in the 1850s. The idealised image of 'Merrie England' came largely from books like Chaucer's **Canterbury Tales** and Malory's **Morte d'Arthur**, from which this scene is taken. May blossom had always been symbolic of renewal and the coming of Spring, the visit of Queen Guinevere carrying May boughs brought a blessing upon all the places visited.

The artist John Collier studied art at the Slade School in London, in Paris and in Munich. He was also a writer on the theory and history of art.

CAH

THE HON. JOHN COLLIER (1850-1934)

The Right Hon. Samuel Cunliffe Lister (Baron Masham of Swinton) 1901

Oil on canvas 127 x 102 cm

Presented by the Lord Mayor, William C.Lupton, for the City of Bradford in 1901

1901-1

Collier was commissioned to paint a portrait of Samuel Cunliffe Lister (Lord Masham) in 1901. Cunliffe Lister is shown with the disputed combing machine (the Square Motion Comb) in a portrait painted for display at Cartwright Hall.

CAH

HERBERT DRAPER (1864-1920)

The Golden Fleece 1904

Oil on canvas 155 x 272.5 cm

Purchased from the artist in 1905

1905-11

Roman mythology was an important source for 19th century artists. The story of Jason and the Golden Fleece occurs in the *Metamorphoses* of the Roman poet Ovid. The dispossessed Prince Jason was set a number of impossible tasks to regain his father's throne. While trying to recover the Golden Fleece from its keeper, the king's daughter Medea, who was also a witch, fell in love with Jason and helped him, taking her brother with them as hostage. During the chase, she threw her brother overboard to delay the pursuing ship. Draper has painted this scene with many dynamic figures using the diagonals of the boy's body and the oars with the arms of the straining rowers to construct the composition. The paint surface is equally dynamic, the paint applied with a heavily loaded brush and vigorous brushstrokes, rejecting the smooth, even surface favoured by many 19th century painters.

Draper studied at the Royal Academy in London and in Paris at the Academie Julien; he was much influenced by the technique of Titian.

CAH

ALFRED ELMORE (1815-1881)

The Invention of the Combing Machine 1862

Oil on canvas 100 x 141 cm

Purchased in 1982

F1982-84

The combing machine was an invention crucial to the Industrial Revolution. Like so many innovations, it had more than one inventor. It is attributed to the English clergyman Dr Edmund Cartwright (1743-1823) as well as Joseph Heilman of Alsace. Here, Heilman is shown at the moment of inspiration, watching his daughter using a comb to remove the tangles from her hair. He then devised a machine which used a similar technique to comb sheep's wool, making it easier and faster to spin.

This picture first belonged to Colonel Akroyd, the Halifax manufacturer. It was then bought by Sir Isaac Holden of Bradford for his house Oakworth Hall near Keighley. Elmore was an artist born in Ireland who came to England to study at the Royal Academy Schools. He studied in Paris, Munich and Rome finally settling in London where he became a stalwart of the Royal Academy.

CAH

THOMAS GAINSBOROUGH (1727-1788)

Portrait of Sir Francis Basset early 1760s

Oil on canvas 128 x 102.5 cm

Purchased in 1959

1959-2

Francis Basset (1715-1769) was a member of a prominent Cornish mine-owning family. This portrait was probably painted in the early 1760s when Gainsborough was working in Bath, then as fashionable a centre as London. Gainsborough was born in Sudbury in Suffolk and apprenticed in London to Gravelot the engraver and later, the painter Francis Hayman. Gainsborough set up his own studio in London, at first meeting with little success. He returned to Sudbury, then moved to Bath in 1759 where he worked for 14 years establishing a reputation. This success enabled him to set up another London studio, and this time to become Reynolds' greatest rival, his chief asset being his skill at depicting gorgeous silks and lace. Much has been made of the rivalry between the two artists. Reynolds wrote ambiguously of Gainsborough's work after his death "this chaos, this uncouth and shapeless appearance, by a kind of magic, at a certain distance assumes form..."

CAH

AMAL GHOSH (born 1933)

Flight II 1995

Oil on canvas 183 x 152.5 cm

Purchased in 1995 and funded from the proceeds of the National Lottery through the Arts Council of England

F1995-21

Flight II is one of a series of paintings exploring universal traumas of dispossession and loss. To Amal Ghosh, flight can mean "fleeing from" or "rising above".

Flight II presents us with a dual world of matter and spirit symbolised by the light and dark horses. The female rider also appears to have a dual aspect. She is clothed but suspended before her is a naked, apparently flying figure. The diminutive male figure with the startling bird's head represents another kind of duality between the animal and human world. In spite of a quality of menace about the various images, there is also a feeling of buoyancy and hope

reinforced by the vibrant life-affirming red of the background. Ghosh was born in West Bengal in India. He studied art in both Calcutta and London.

NPS

JOHN ATKINSON GRIMSHAW (1836-1893)

Fiamella/Fiametta 1883

Oil on canvas 61 x 46 cm

Purchased in 1978 with the assistance of the National Art Collections Fund and the Friends of Bradford Art Galleries and Museums

F1978-1

The Leeds artist Atkinson Grimshaw is best known for his misty views of northern suburbs and docks. Here, he treats a medieval subject in a classical style. Fiamella was the name given by the medieval Italian poet Boccaccio to Maria d'Aquino, the woman he loved but did not marry. She is shown here in front of a marble frieze of classical figures with trailing ivy.

Painted in Atkinson Grimshaw's customary fine technique, with no visible brushstrokes, this smoothness of handling led one contemporary writer to comment that "...not a few artists were doubtful whether they could be accepted as paintings at all". Grimshaw was one of the few artists who admitted using a camera as an aid to composition.

CAH

FREDERICK HALL (1860-1948)

The Drinking Pool c. 1898

Oil on canvas 73.5 x 160.5 cm

Purchased from the artist in 1898

1898-1

The Drinking Pool is typical of Hall's subject-matter, which was dominated by the portrayal of rural life and landscapes. Individual strokes of violet, blue, pink and pastel greens are used to produce an evanescent and poetic quality strongly influenced by French Impressionism.

Fred Hall was born in Stillington, Yorkshire, but later moved to Lincolnshire where he attended Lincoln School of Art. He then studied at the Antwerp Academy of Fine Arts where he met Frank Bramley and Edwin Harris, later returning to England with them to join the Newlyn colony of artists, where he lived for the rest of his life.

CAH

SALIMA HASHMI (born 1942)

Zones of Dreams 1996

Tea wash, gold leaf, acrylic and collage on paper

152 x 306 cm (triptych, each panel 152 x 102 cm)

Purchased in 1996 with funding from the proceeds of the

National Lottery through the Arts Council of England

F1996-22

The pictographic map-making traditions of the East and West are both drawn upon in this beautiful piece. By using archeological and architectural references the artist has managed to combine reality with a mythic imagination. The vast Indian sub-continent, including Pakistan, Bangladesh, Sri Lanka, Bhutan and Nepal are accurately enough located and depicted. The sub-continent glows a golden orange, hemmed by emerald green waters that seem to almost completely engulf Sri Lanka. The turbulent seas are populated by multi-hued fish and an Iranian phoenix straight out of fabula. Cities are identified through their traditions - a delicate embroidered paisley for Lucknow and jali motifs for Agra. Bangladesh is covered by lotus blossom, a reminder of how lush and beauteous this region was. Sanskrit and Persian inscriptions taken from old Hindu and Muslim manuscripts celebrate a pluralism that was an integral part of the cultural development of the sub continent. This map is a strange and rich creation at once wonderfully subtle and dramatic. Salima Hashmi lives in Lahore where she is Principal of the National College of Arts.

NPS

DAVID HOCKNEY (born 1937)

Bolton Junction, Eccleshill 1956

Oil on panel 122 x 101.5 cm

Presented by Mrs Taylor in 1984

F1984-59

Painted during Hockney's early years at the Bradford School of Art, this landscape view is typical of his work in the 1950s. The grey/green palette with trees and figures outlined in black are characteristic of the style of the 1950s, popularly known as the 'Kitchen Sink' school.

During his four years at the Bradford School of Art, Hockney received a traditional, academic art training that emphasised drawing and painting from life as well as the study of perspective and anatomy. Students were encouraged to study the work of Degas and the British Post Impressionists, particularly W R Sickert and the Euston Road School.

Hockney's pictures of Bradford suburbs are reminiscent of Sickert's London street paintings. Sickert's choice of everyday subject matter, an emphasis on observing tonal values, clear compositional structure and love of surface texture can all be seen in **Bolton Junction, Eccleshill**.

CAH

BALRAJ KHANNA (born 1940)

Nursery Rhymes - for Dmitri 1997

Acrylic, sand and card on wood base 183 x 183 cm

Purchased in 1997 with funding from the proceeds of the

National Lottery through the Arts Council of England

F1997-3

The aerial shapes that float in Khanna's earlier works have been isolated, defined and painted in vivid colours and arranged in rows on pristine white board like a pictographic abacus. The shapes suggest bird, animal and aquatic forms. This enchanting work has a charming title. Balraj Khanna is a self-taught artist, he lives in London.

NPS

HENRY HERBERT LA THANGUE (1859-1929)

In the Orchard c.1893

Oil on canvas 83 x 72.5 cm

Purchased in 1894

1894-4

Henry La Thangue's associations with the city of Bradford were officially recognised in 1894 when **In the Orchard** was bought for Cartwright Hall. This painting of La Thangue's wife with a friend in the orchard at their home in Sussex is one of La Thangue's most impressionistic works. It contrasts with the starkness of the muted indoor light of **The Connoisseur**. The light effects were noted in *The Times* where the critic praised "the sunshine flecking the grass and the branches, and shining through the shadows cast by the leaves".

La Thangue attended the Royal Academy Schools and then, like many artists of his generation, went to Paris to complete his artistic education at the Ecole des Beaux Arts. In Paris, he was influenced by the popular artist, Bastien-Lepage who advocated that artists should paint entirely out of doors.

CAH

HENRY HERBERT LA THANGUE (1859-1929)

The Connoisseur 1887

Oil on canvas 114 x 160 cm

Presented by Mrs V.H.Mitchell in 1948

BH11-48

La Thangue returned to England in 1884 and came to Bradford where his work was bought by many local collectors including the worsted manufacturer, Abraham Mitchell. In 1887 La Thangue painted this group portrait of Abraham Mitchell and his family. They are shown in the private art gallery adjoining their home 'Bowling Park' in Rooley Lane. Mitchell sits, engrossed in the painting on the easel before him. On the walls hang other pictures from his collection.

The limited use of colour is typical of La Thangue's starkly realistic paintings of the 1880s and early 1890s. While **The Connoisseur** has some affinity with the tradition of the 18th century conversation piece, a more likely source of inspiration is Alma-Tadema's **A Picture Gallery** of 1874 (Townley Art Gallery, Burnley).

CAH

CHARLES LIDDERDALE (1831-1895)

Rejected Addresses 1876

Oil on canvas 128 x 86.5 cm

Presented in 1931 by Sir Frederick Ackroyd

1931-26

Lidderdale was a successful genre painter based in London who exhibited regularly at the Royal Academy. According to Christopher Wood, he specialised in painting works smaller than this, especially "pretty farm girls". Here, a pretty girl of more exalted rank in mock 18th century garments hesitates at a slightly open gate. The title **Rejected Addresses** suggests that she has just turned down a suitor. She hesitates, considering whether she has made the right decision, the slightly open gate echoing her indecision. There is still time to change her mind; the viewer is invited to imagine the rest of the story.

CAH

JAMES LOBLEY (1828-1888)

The Dole, Stow Church c.1867

Oil on panel 50.5 x 71 cm

Purchased in 1920

1920-19

The life and work of the genre painter James Lobley, is closely linked with the artistic development of Bradford. Born in Hull in 1828, by 1846 he had moved to Leeds where he entered the Leeds Government School. Lobley's talent was quickly recognised, he gained the highest award for design and was, in 1849, appointed as teacher of design at the Mechanics Institute in Bradford. He had many local patrons but constantly struggled against ill-health and poverty. His favourite subjects were church interiors which he painted both in oils and in watercolours, generally in a style that owed a great deal to Thomas Webster. The distribution of Tomlinson's Dole began at Stow in Lincolnshire. The ancient charity allowed 2s. per week for the provision of bread for the needy. This was distributed every Sunday after the service.

CAH

EDWIN LONG (1829-1891)

An Egyptian Feast 1877

Oil on canvas 189 x 381 cm

Presented by Mrs Janet Lund in 1931

1931-35

An Egyptian Feast was first exhibited in 1877 at the Royal Academy in London accompanied by a chilling text from the writings of the Roman historian Herodotus. The scene seems designed to show a range of different reactions to the dummy corpse, from the indifference of the young to the thoughtful expressions of the two elderly figures. The young dancer leaning at the left looks directly out at the viewer inviting the viewer's reaction.

Long used small stageset models to compose his pictures giving them a theatrical atmosphere. A self-taught artist, he had made regular visits to Spain between 1857 and 1873 in search of subjects. This left him with an admiration for the brown tones frequently used by Spanish artists.

An Egyptian Feast was begun after a visit to Egypt in 1877. Some of the artefacts shown are still in the collection of the British Museum which was being expanded at this period by the collecting activities of Victorian explorers and archaeologists.

CAH

L.S.LOWRY (1887-1976)

Industrial Landscape (Ashton-under-Lyne) 1952

Oil on canvas 115 x 152.5 cm

Purchased in 1957

1957-1

Lowry's unique vision was not recognised until his retirement from work at the age of 65. Rejected as a student by the Manchester College of Art, Lowry became a clerk, studying art at evening classes with the French artist Adolphe Valette, who had settled in Manchester. By 1920, Lowry had evolved his style and subject, industrial Northern towns painted in a simplified, schematic manner with minute, stick-like figures.

After his retirement in 1952, Lowry was able to give more time to his artistic career, and his reputation increased. He was also a painter of empty, melancholic landscape scenes which have, until recently, been under-rated.

CAH

BERTRAM PRIESTMAN (1868-1951)

The Heart of the West Riding 1916

Oil on canvas 115.5 x 184 cm

Presented by the artist in 1918

1918-1

Bertram Priestman was born into a wealthy Bradford manufacturing family. In his youth he was much influenced by his older half brother Arnold Priestman, who had been a pupil of Henry La Thangue. After a tour of Italy in 1886, Bertram Priestman attended Bradford Technical College followed in 1888 by the Slade School of Art. He began exhibiting at the Royal Academy in 1889 and at the New English Art Club from 1894.

His broad and vigorous handling of paint reflects the influence of French Impressionism upon his style. His paintings of landscapes and coastal scenes combined the English landscape tradition with French techniques using a bright luminous palette. He lived in London and Suffolk, painting his native Yorkshire and East Anglia.

CAH

GUIDO RENI (1575-1642)

The Flight into Egypt

Oil on canvas 160 x 129.3 cm

Purchased in 1966 with the assistance of the Victoria and Albert Museum Purchase Grant Fund

1966-20

Reni trained in Bologna in the studio of the Carraci. On his removal to Rome he was quickly acclaimed as the greatest artist of his day. His religious works were classical in style but have become debased by an association with sentimental religious images.

A withdrawn and devout man, Reni, was also a passionate gambler, and despite an enormously lucrative and productive career he died in poverty.

The Flight into Egypt is painted in his early style although it has been suggested that the putto with flowers at bottom right was added later in the broader and more fluid manner of his late work. This has had the effect of making the Virgin appear less introspective.

CAH

JOSHUA REYNOLDS (1723-1792)

Master Thomas Lister, "The Brown Boy" 1764

Oil on canvas 231 x 147.5 cm

Presented by H.M.Treasury in 1976

1976-59

Thomas Lister was twelve years old when painted by Reynolds as the heir to the Lister family estate of Gisburn Park near Clitheroe. He wears the so-called 'Vandyke', costume, loosely imitating the dress of the courtiers of Charles I. His pose is derived from the classical **Apollo Sauroctonos** which Renolds probably saw on his visit to Rome in 1751-2.

The Brown Boy hung at Gisburn until 1889 when it was purchased by Samuel Cunliffe Lister (later Lord Masham), for his new home Swinton Castle in North Yorkshire. The painting remained at Swinton until 1976, when it passed in lieu of Estate Duty to H.M.Treasury, and thence to Cartwright Hall.

CAH

WILLIAM ROBERTS (1895-1980)

Jockeys/The Paddock 1928

Oil on canvas 122.5 x 92.5 cm

Presented by the Contemporary Art Society in 1935

1935-23

Roberts' distinctive, mature style had developed by the end of the 1920s. The angularity of the pre-War Vorticist works had disappeared but these later works still have that same self-contained, rhythmic quality. Roberts' figures have a tubular, mechanical appearance, deriving perhaps from the work of Leger. Their limbs form chains of pattern as they go about their daily business. His subjects were generally proletarian, here, a member of the upper classes is also included. His sombre clothes contrast with the gaily coloured silks of the jockeys. Holding the skittish horse firmly by the bridle, he is the anchor of the composition. William Roberts began his career as an apprentice in an advertising firm. He attended evening classes soon winning a scholarship to the Slade School of Art in London. He met and became a member of the 'English Cubist' group the Vorticists with Edward Wadsworth and Wyndham Lewis. His early work was almost abstract, by the 1930s the figures had become more sculptural.

CAH

GEORGE ROMNEY (1734-1802)

Portrait of Dr James Ainslie of Kendal c.1765-80

Oil on canvas 145 x 121 cm

Purchased in 1908

1908-28

Dr Ainslie was a distinguished physician in Kendal, where Romney lived for five years immediately after his apprenticeship. The doctor is portrayed here, not with the instruments of his profession but, as a man of culture. The leatherbound volumes and classical bust allude to his learning in other spheres. The graceful appearance of the figure confirms Romney's reputation as a leading portraitist of the period.

Born in Northumberland and trained in Edinburgh, Dr Ainslie had moved to Kendal in 1765, then one of the most prosperous towns in the North of England. This portrait was probably painted during one of Romney's frequent return visits.

A native of nearby Dalton-in-Furness, Romney moved to Kendal, then an important town in 1734 where he became apprenticed to the painter Christopher Steele.

Romney moved to London in 1762 and quickly became a fashionable painter and a rival to Sir Joshua Reynolds. He composed 'High Art' subjects on classical and allegorical themes. The notorious Lady Hamilton was his favourite model.

CAH

WILLIAM ROTHENSTEIN (1878-1945)

Self Portrait c.1906

Oil on canvas 102 x 89 cm

Presented by the artist's brother, Charles Rutherston in 1925

1925-2

William Rothenstein and his younger brothers Albert and Charles (later to change their names to Rutherston) were born in Bradford. Both William and Albert studied at the Slade School in London, where Albert was a contemporary of Augustus John. John became an intimate friend of William Rothenstein and this friendship continued for many years, in spite of John's increasingly unconventional lifestyle. Rothenstein here takes a dispassionate, unflattering look at himself in his 50s, a tight-lipped figure with a skin of greenish hue. His pose is static and thoughtful, the result of deep contemplation.

CAH

JAMINI ROY (1887-1972)

Panch Kanya

Five plants c.1943-1944

Gouache on paper 28.8 x 30.5 cm each

Purchased in 1986

F11-86; F7-86

Midway through a flourishing career Jamini Roy changed from oils to gouache and the folk art techniques of his native Bengal. This move was dictated by concerns of both aesthetics and identity. Roy employs a deft line and imbues what could be static images with considerable vigour. The colours are bright and confidently applied. **Panch Kanya** and **Five plants**, like the rest of Roy's work, manage to draw very directly from traditional art, particularly the art of patua or scroll painting, without in any way appearing to be nostalgic. Roy was born a Hindu but was extremely interested in other religions as well. Episodes from Christ's life were a frequent theme in his work. **Panch Kanya**, which also means five maidens, could be a reference to the biblical tale of the five wise and five foolish virgins waiting to welcome the bridegroom with lamps. The plant in **Five plants** could be the tulsi plant which is sacred to Hindus.

NPS

GODFRIED SCHALCKEN (1643-1706)

Saint Peter by Candlelight 1700-6

Oil on canvas 61.5 x 48 cm

Purchased in 1964

1964-14

Schalcken was schooled in the meticulous art of genre painting by Rembrandt's former pupils, Hoogstraten and Dou in Leyden. He had a brilliant career as a portraitist and painter of mythological subjects. He established himself in London in the 1690s, but become court painter at Dusseldorf towards the end of his life.

St. Peter is identifiable by his key, the emblem of his authority and mission. He is clearly seen in Protestant terms as a common man rather than as founder of the Papacy. The artist specialised in depicting figures by candlelight.

According to the 18th century connoisseur, Horace Walpole, Schalcken's method was to shut his models and sitters in a dark chamber, using a viewing hole in order to paint them. This, of course, enabled him to paint in daylight.

CAH

AMRITA SHER-GIL (1913-41)

Portrait of a Woman 1939

Watercolour on paper 27 x 18 cm

Presented anonymously in 1991

F1991-74

Amrita Sher-Gil, after having trained in Paris, travelled extensively all over India, studying the cave art of Ajanta, Ellora and Amaravati. She was critical of contemporary Indian artists who mechanically reproduced paintings in the miniature tradition or mimicked European themes without properly understanding them. Sher-Gil was part Hungarian and part Sikh and therefore heir to both traditions. She was profoundly influenced by the work of Gauguin and both India and its art fascinated her. In this rather mysterious portrait, the influence of Ajanta cave paintings is clearly discernable, in the earthy shades and the features of the woman with her pale lips and long fine eyebrows. Sher-Gil died tragically young and her premature death was a loss to modern Indian art.

NPS

GURMINDER SIKAND (born 1960)

Landscape with Woman and Tree 1995

Watercolour and gouache on paper 30 x 42 cm

Purchased in 1996 and funded from the proceeds of the National Lottery through the Arts Council of England

F1996.2

Gurminder Sikand's works are, in the main, informed by myth, dream and the folk arts of Mithila and Kalighat. Her childhood was spent, largely in the outdoors, in Kasauli in the Punjab. The landscape is often anthropomorphosised and mysterious faces frequently loom in the background. The women who appear in the works seem to emerge from the landscape. The colours are lucid, watery and delicate. Sikand is now based in Nottingham.

NPS

SHAHZIA SIKANDER (born 1971)

Riding the Written 1993

Screenprint, pigment and tea wash on wasli 37 x 25.5 cm

Purchased in 1995 with support from the MGC/V&A Purchase Grant Fund and the National Art Collections Fund

F1995-17

Shahzia Sikander gained her first arts degree in the technique of miniature painting from the National College of Arts in Lahore. She subsequently gained a further degree in printmaking from the Rhode Island College of Design. **Riding the Written** and **Untitled IV**, also produced in 1993, reflect her various concerns. In **Riding the Written**, minute horses thunder off the sheet onto the moody indigo borders. Starting as a row of zoomorphic calligraphic creatures or skeleton-like horses, they progress down the sheet in fractured rows. There is great animation, indeed chaos in the little figures. Some of them seem to be truncated, the heads separated from the bodies yet disconcertingly mobile. The resonances are immediate. They recall moments of great upheaval in history - Mongol raids perhaps or the Partition of 1947 with its tragic consequences.

NPS

FRANCIS NEWTON SOUZA (born 1924)

Bradford 1958

Oil on board 122 x 60.5 cm

Purchased in 1993 with support from the MGC/V&A Purchase Grant Fund

F1993-4

In style and treatment this painting is similar to David Hockney's **Bolton Junction, Eccleshill** painted in 1956. Both works have a grey-green palette reflecting the 'Kitchen Sink' school of painting current in the 1950s. Souza's Goan Catholic heritage surfaces in the crosses that surmount the buildings in this picture. The cross makes a frequent appearance in his work.

NPS

C.J.STANILAND (1838-1916)

The Emigrant Ship 1880s

Oil on canvas 104 x 176 cm

Presented by Frederick Priestman in 1913

Staniland is best known as a draughtsman whose work was illustrated in popular journals. His skill as a draughtsman is seen in the composition of this picture, the gaze and gestures of the figures on shore leading the eye of the viewer towards those on board the ship itself, the whole creating a human waterfall of nets and clambering figures. Crowded genre scenes in the style of William Frith were immensely popular with the Victorian public and frequently mass-produced as prints.

Staniland studied at Birmingham School of Art and the Royal Academy Schools and exhibited frequently in London and his native Hull. He was a prolific illustrator in contemporary journals, such as the **Illustrated London News** and the **Graphic**.

CAH

PHILIP WILSON STEER (1860-1942)

The End of the Chapter 1911

Oil on canvas 120.5 x 143 cm

Purchased in 1912

1912-6

Steer had been a vigorous exponent of the ideals of modern French painting in England in the late 1880s and early 1890s. He had trained at the Academie Julien in Paris and was a founder member of the New English Art Club in 1886. He taught painting at the Slade for nearly 40 years. On his return to England, he lived in the 1880s at Walberswick, an artist colony on the Suffolk coast, producing beach and seascapes, which echoed the neo-Impressionism of Seurat. Although painted in 1911, the girl's hair and clothes belong in style to the late 1880s or 90s. The yellow cover of the book she has laid down identifies it as a French novel, then slightly risqué reading for a respectable young woman.

CAH

GIORGIO VASARI (1511-1574)

The Holy Family with St.John c.1545

Oil on panel 141 x 113 cm

Purchased in 1966 with the assistance of the Victoria and Albert Museum Purchase Fund

1966-18

A pupil and fervent admirer of Michelangelo, Vasari is now chiefly known for his 'Lives' of Italian Renaissance painters. He was an architect and painter of exuberant ability and high ambition - the archetypal Mannerist artist. Probably intended as an altarpiece to be hung above eye level, the painting has a number of details borrowed from the work of other artists. The huge muscular hands of St. Elizabeth imitate Michelangelo, and the colour scheme and proportions of the Virgin's body are consciously distorted. Yet **The Holy Family** must have been painted with fluency and speed in accordance with Vasari's notion of working with a burst of energy, in a state of almost divine inspiration.

CAH

JAMES WARD (1769-1859)

Gordale Scar 1813

Oil on canvas 76 x 102 cm

Purchased in 1904

1904-6

The spectacular rock formation of Gordale Scar has inspired amateur and professional artists as diverse as James Ward and, more recently, David Hockney. It was particularly admired by lovers of the sublime in the 18th and early 19th century.

This oil study for the finished painting in the Tate was commissioned around 1811 by Lord Ribblesdale of Gisburn Park, (co-incidentally, the son of "The Brown Boy"). Ward, a self-taught artist, spent three years making studies of Gordale Scar as well as studies of cattle, before completing the massive canvas in 1814.

At this point, Ward was at the height of his career and had recently been elected a full Academician. Considered the greatest animal painter of his time he was also an accomplished landscape artist as revealed here by his dramatic, moody evocation of Gordale Scar.

CAH

CHRISTOPHER WOOD (1901-1930)

The Manicure (Portrait of Frosca Munster) 1929

Oil on canvas 152.5 x 102 cm

Presented by the Contemporary Art Society in 1935

1935-24

Christopher Wood died under the wheels of a train barely a year after painting this portrait of his mistress, Frosca Munster, in 1929. Best known for his poetic landscapes of Brittany and Cornwall, he had initially studied architecture at Liverpool University. During this time, legend has it, he met Augustus John who persuaded him to become an artist. The association with John rapidly introduced him to fashionable society in London and then Paris, where he encountered the work of Picasso and Matisse. He remained in Paris, enrolling at the Academie Julien, his studies frequently interrupted by journeys with friends throughout Europe and North Africa; he also succumbed to opium addiction.

In 1926 Wood travelled to Cornwall where he met Ben and Winifred Nicholson for the first time. In 1928 he met the married Russian exile Frosca Munster who is shown in **The Manicure**. The picture also includes two pots of flowers which are a reference to the work of Winifred Nicholson. Wood returned to Cornwall to paint later in 1928. He spent part of 1929, just before his death, painting in Brittany. It is for these last landscapes of Cornwall and Brittany that he is best remembered.

CAH

TOM WOOD (born 1955)

Naked Self Portrait 1978

Acrylic on canvas 61 x 61 cm

Presented by Arthur Haigh in 1984

F1984-45

Portraits were an important part of Tom Wood's early career. Here, he shows himself in a traditional 'bathroom mirror' view with the added meticulously-painted still life detail of a wire coat-hanger.

Tom Wood was born in Tanganyika (now Tanzania), East Africa. He came to the north of England in 1959 where he studied graphic design at Leeds Polytechnic. From 1986-88, he worked at Cartwright Hall as a part-time Education Officer.

CAH

ROBERT WYLIE (1839-1877)

A Breton Sorceress c.1872

Oil on canvas 91.5 x 119.5 cm

Presented by the family of the late Alfred Harris in 1906

1906-37

Robert Wylie was the most able and distinguished of a colony of American painters who settled at Pont-Aven in Brittany during the 1860s and 70s. In an Industrial age, they pursued a Romantic fascination with the unique and ancient customs of the Breton people.

The Breton Sorceress was awarded a medal in the Salon of 1872 and established Wylie's reputation on the Continent and in America, ensuring that everything he painted sold quickly.

The story behind the scene is obscure. The old woman is perhaps casting the baby's fortune, but there are sinister overtones. Although the peasant costumes are painted in meticulous detail and an intensity of mood is conveyed, Wylie's attitude to the powerful superstitions which governed the Breton people is ambiguous.

CAH

DRAWINGS

DAVID BOMBERG (1890-1957)

The Chinaman 1921

Watercolour 40.5 x 56 cm

Presented by the Contemporary Art Society in 1927

1927-42

This luminous watercolour has more in common with contemporary productions of Duncan Grant and other contributors to the Omega Workshops than with Bomberg's own work of the period. The subject, a figure reclining in a landscape background, could easily have found its way onto an Omega Workshop screen or cupboard door; the title was probably applied after completion because of a chance resemblance.

The angular, cubistic work of Bomberg's Vorticist period had given way to a softer, more lyrical style. The excitement of the `Machine Age' was now discredited by the destruction wrought by the Great War. A growing interest in landscape led Bomberg to Palestine in 1923 and then to Spain and Russia. He spent the next years travelling with the occasional return to London to raise funds by selling pictures. Bomberg's work was bought enthusiastically by Bradford collectors, through the agency of the dealer Alfred Willey who made regular buying trips to London on behalf of local collectors.

Bomberg was born into a Jewish family which had fled from Poland. Through economic necessity, he was apprenticed to a chromolithographer, but he also attended evening classes run by Walter Bayes and later, W R Sickert. He then became a life model at the Slade School, where he was eventually accepted as a student in 1911. It was here that he met the other young artists who were to form the Vorticist group.

CAH

FORD MADOX BROWN (1821-1893)

Romeo and Juliet 1876

Pen, ink and black chalk on paper 71 x 52.5 cm

Presented by Asa Lingard in 1926

1926-105

One of four versions of the same subject drawn by Ford Madox Brown in the late 1860s and 1870s, the finished oil painting was commissioned by the Newcastle manufacturer James Leathart. Leathart, like Dunlop in Bradford, bought pictures direct from the artist. He had a particular enthusiasm for the work of the Pre-Raphaelites. As was his habit, Brown made a number of alterations to the painting after a period of several months, particularly to Juliet's head. After the completion of the purchase there was a slightly acrimonious exchange with Leathart, who

had committed, in the artists opinion, the crime of hanging the painting over a fireplace.

CAH

EDWARD BURNE-JONES (1833-1898)

Cushion studies c.1884

Chalk on paper

Bequest of Mrs Constance Rea in 1953

1953-2

EDWARD BURNE-JONES (1833-1898)

Hair studies c.1890

Chalk on paper

Presented by W.T.Vint in 1919

1919-20

Burne-Jones was a fluid draughtsman, which perhaps explains his success as a designer of stained glass and textiles. These cushions were probably drawn as ideas for the painting **King Cophetua and the Beggar Maid** (Tate Gallery) while the hair studies have an affinity with the final figure of the Queen in **Arthur of Avalon** (Ponce Museum of Art, Puerto Rico).

Burne-Jones originally intended to enter the church, until he met William Morris at Oxford in the 1850s. They toured the cathedrals of northern France in 1855 and moved to London in 1856 soon after meeting Rossetti. They were involved in the early productions of Morris, Marshall, Faulkner & Co., which was established in 1861. Burne-Jones was to be a prolific designer of stained glass and textiles for `The Firm'.

CAH

ANISH KAPOOR (born 1954)

Untitled 1990

Ink, acrylic and pigment on paper 76.5 x 55 cm

Presented by the Contemporary Art Society in 1992

F1992-7

Kapoor views drawing as a very separate activity from sculpture and tends not to display the two together. The textural quality of the pigment and the deep spice colours give the drawings a visceral quality. The secret and sacred heights and recesses of mountains and caves were an important factor of the drawings Kapoor produced during this period. They seem to be paradigms of the human body, particularly the female form. This is clearly expressed in this powerful drawing.

NPS

PETER LELY (1618-1680)

Portrait of the Artist   c. 1660-70

Sepia on paper 25 x 19 cm

Purchased in 1920

(1920-14)

Lely was born near Utrecht in the Low Countries and came to England in 1641, the year of the death of Van Dyck, court painter to Charles I. Lely painted portraits of members of the court, he also purchased pictures for Charles I who had an extensive art collection. After the execution of Charles I in 1649, Lely continued to work during Cromwell's Parliament and for Charles II after his eventual succession in 1660. He became court painter to Charles II in 1661.

He drew this self-portrait on one side of a sheet of paper, then used the heavy ink outline to re-create himself in a gentlemanly pose on the verso.

CAH

DANTE GABRIEL ROSSETTI (1828-1882)

La Donna della Finestra 1870

Pastel on paper (Surtees 255A) 85 x 72 cm

Presented by Asa Lingard in 1921

1921-43

Rossetti spent long periods working on paintings, making frequent studies for the subject. This study which is more finished than others, is of Jane, the wife of William Morris. Here she looks down with compassion on the poet Dante who mourns the death of his love Beatrice. The inscription is a line taken from Dante's 12th century poem `Vita Nuova' which chronicles this love. Rossetti had translated Dante's work into English. The final painting (Fogg Museum of Art, Harvard University) was not completed until 1879, it differs little from this study.

Rossetti studied at the Royal Academy Schools in the 1840s. He then spent a short time as a pupil of Ford Madox Brown. He was instrumental in founding the Pre-Raphaelite Brotherhood late in the 1840s.

CAH

DANTE GABRIEL ROSSETTI (1828-1882)

Study for the head of the Dead Beatrice in the painting "Dante's Dream on the day of the death of Beatrice" 1871

Chalk on paper (Surtees 81 R 1F) 57 x 51 cm

Purchased in 1921

1921-43

Mrs William Morris was again the model for this drawing although Mrs James Hannay also sat for the figure. The subject again is Dante's `Vita Nuova'. In the finished painting (Aberdeen Art Gallery), the body of Beatrice lies on a bier, Dante is led into the chamber by the figure of Love, two women lower a pall covered with may blossom to reveal the dead Beatrice. The floor is strewn with red poppies, symbolic of death.

TOM WOOD (born 1955)

Portrait of Elaine at the Schlossmuseum 1978

Acrylic on paper 25.5 x 50 cm

Presented by Arthur Haigh in 1984

F1984-46

Tom Wood's work has always been informed by art historical references. His wife Elaine is shown in the Schlossmuseum at Darmstadt in front of Holbein's painting the **Meyer Madonna**. She merges into the background almost absorbed into, but still distinct from, Holbein's masterpiece which is treated in a flat, modernistic style giving the illusion of an out of focus slide projected onto the background. A velvet curtain has been reverently drawn aside to reveal both Elaine and the Holbein. Curiously, neither of the Woods had ever visited Darmstadt.

CAH

Zoomorphic horse

Iran Late 18th or early 19th century

Ink, paint and gold leaf on paper 17 x 22.8 cms.

Purchased in 1994

F1994.92

Calligraphy is a major art form in all Muslim cultures. In addition to works on paper, calligraphy was also an important integral embellishment of architecture, textiles, stone and metalware. Zoomorphic birds and animals using calligraphy are very much part of the Iranian art tradition. However, the use of calligraphy to form figurative shapes is particularly strong among the Shia sects of Iran, Turkey and the Indian sub-continent.

The central motif in this image translates into *SAIF I ALI AL ZULFIQAR* or the sword of Ali. The horse is on a speckled background, the sword form picked out in blue with floral decorations. There are five couplets in Farsi in the decorated borders. The calligraphy embodies both sacred and secular text.

NPS

PRINTS AND PHOTOGRAPHS

NUDRAT AFZA (born 1955)

Cartwright Hall and Lister Park 1996

Colour prints 48 x 32 cm each

Purchased in 1996 with funding from the proceeds of the
National Lottery through the Arts Council of England

F1996-11; F1996-12

Nudrat Afza is a self-taught photographer based in Bradford. In 1996 she was commissioned to produce ten photographs of Cartwright Hall and its grounds, a building she knows and loves. Although Afza's photography usually involves people interacting with each other or going about the business of living, her works are characterised by a non-voyeuristic quality. The rest of the series on Cartwright Hall includes moving studies of people engrossed with the building or the park. Afza has demonstrated that she can capture an evocative atmosphere in both landscape and architectural shots. She has exhibited regionally and nationally.

NPS

JIRI ANDERELE (born 1936)

Elite (Cyclus Soldiers - Illusion and Reality) 1982

Mixed media (edition of 70)   95.6 x 63.8 cm

Purchased in 1982

F1982-109

Born in Pavlikov, Czechoslovakia, Anderle was educated at the Academy of Fine Arts in Prague. His delicate intaglio prints have won him frequent prizes at the Biennales of Cracow, Fredrikstad and Ljubljana. He exhibited at the British International Print Biennales of 1982, 1984 and 1986.

CK

GEORG BASELITZ (born 1938)

Bent Figure with Stick 1984

Woodcut (edition of 12)   64.5 x 49.5 cm

Purchased in 1984 with the assistance of the Victoria and Albert
Museum Purchase Grant Fund

F1984-17

Born Hans Georg Kern in Deutschbaselitz in the former GDR, the artist studied painting at the Hochschule fur bildende Kunst, East Berlin. He was expelled for 'social and political immaturity' but continued his studies in West Berlin where he moved in 1957. He adopted the name Georg Baselitz in 1962, the year of his exhibition and manifesto 'Pandemonium'. Much of his art has been concerned with a breaking with tradition and a determination to be unconventional. Perhaps the best example is his practice, begun in 1970, of inverting paintings and prints. Baselitz has exhibited internationally. He became widely known in Britain through exhibitions such as 'A New Spirit in Painting'

(Royal Academy 1981). **Bent Figure with Stick** was exhibited in the Eighth British International Print Biennale.

CK

ANTHONY BENJAMIN (born 1931)

Yellow Arch Style 1969

Screenprint (edition of 30)   103 x 72 cm

Purchased in 1971

CC2:71.5

Anthony Benjamin's initial training was in Engineering Science. After abandoning this for art, he studied with the painter Fernand Leger and the innovative printmaker S W Hayter in Paris. He became well known for screenprints including abstract elements or architectural Art Deco 'quotations'.

CK

WILLIAM BLAKE (1757-1827)

Illustrations to The Book of Job (Plate 14) 1825

Engraving (second edition 1875) 21 x 16cm

Purchased in 1977 with the assistance of the Victoria and Albert
Museum Purchase Grant Fund

F1977-32

William Blake has been described as a visionary; a profoundly reflective man who created his own powerful philosophy and mythology through his poetry and art. He was apprenticed at an early age to the engraver James Basire, then completed his training at the Royal Academy Schools in 1779. An enduring interest in the classical world, together with a thorough grounding in engraving techniques, underpinned all his work. Blake had long pondered the story of Job, producing from 1821 two sets of watercolours and a series of engravings. They reveal a highly personal interpretation of the Old Testament book, where the drama of the Fall and Redemption is acted out in Job's imagination until the final discovery of Eden, through self-knowledge.

CK

PATRICK CAULFIELD (born 1936)

Earthenware 1967

Screenprint on paper (Edition of 75) 53 x 89 cm

Purchased in 1969

E156-69

Shown at the first British International Print Biennale in 1969.

PATRICK CAULFIELD (born 1936)

Poster for Sixth British International Print Biennale

1979

Screenprint (edition of 100) 84 x 59.2 cm

Commissioned for the Sixth British International Print Biennale
in 1979

F1981-67

Patrick Caulfield was born in London. He studied and later
taught at the Chelsea School of Art followed by the Royal
College of Art. He won the Prix de Jeunes Artistes award for
graphics in 1965. Caulfield was as much associated with
printmaking as he was with painting during the 'Pop' era of
the 1960s and early 70s. His firm black outline was
effectively used to describe architectural interiors and still
lives. These were points of departure for compositions
based on a structure of linear design where bright colour
formed a solid background on its own. Caulfield has
exhibited internationally and his work was shown frequently
at the British International Print Biennale.

CK

ANTHONY DAVIES (born 1947)

Brixton / Derry, One Struggle 1981

Lithograph (edition of 16) 45.9 x 37.9 cm

Purchased in 1982

F1982-103

A regular contributor to the British International Print
Biennale, Davies was a prizewinner in 1986 enabling him to
create **The Great Divide**, a series of eight lithographs made
from large aluminium plates. Davies has always been
preoccupied with the observation of ordinary life - often
from the edges. 'Printmaking is always in danger of
becoming too nice, decorative - almost domestic', he wrote
in 1988.

Born in Andover, Hants, Davies trained at Winchester, the
Royal College of Art and the British School at Rome. He has
exhibited both nationally and internationally.

CK

EDWARD DWURNIK (born 1943)

Violence In Town 1978

Lithograph and collage (edition of 5) 69 x 49.5 cm

Purchased in 1979

F1979-53

Born in Radzymin, Poland, Dwurnik was educated at the
Academy of Fine Art in Warsaw. He has exhibited his
paintings and prints in Poland, France, Italy and Germany,
including the Print Biennales of Cracow and Fredrikstad. He
showed **Violence In Town** at Bradford in 1979.

CK

SUSUMU ENDO (born 1933)

Space & Space (Compasses) 1981

Lithograph (edition of 75) 45 x 45cm

Purchased in 1982

F1982-91

Born in Kofu, Japan, Susumu Endo was educated at the
Musashino Design School in Tokyo. He has also worked as a
glass and graphic designer. His prints have been exhibited in
Japan and in the USA. **Space & Space (Compasses)** was
exhibited in the Seventh British International Print Biennale.

CK

FRANCISCO JOSE de GOYA (1746-1828)

The Carnivorous Vulture (plate 76 from `The Disasters of
War') c.1810-1820

Etching 15 x 19 cm

Purchased with the assistance of the Victoria and Albert
Museum Purchase Grant Fund in 1977

F1977-28

Goya's art progressed through periods of lighthearted and
courtly brilliance to the brooding pessimism of his late
works. The prints and paintings of these years are informed
by the isolation caused by deafness and the effects of war.
Los Desastres de la Guerra was produced shortly after
Napoleon's army had marched on Madrid; death, starvation
and acts of cruelty on both sides were commonplace.
Goya was in his sixties when he began the series. Their
power lies in the fact that they do not dwell on the
documentary aspect of war, instead emphasising its
extraordinary capacity to brutalise mankind.

CK

DAVID HOCKNEY (born 1937)

The Boy Hidden in a Fish

plate 4 from **The Little Sea Hare**

(from `Six Fairy Tales From The Brothers Grimm') 1969

Etching and aquatint (edition of 100) 23 x 27 cm

Purchased in 1970 with the assistance of the Victoria and Albert
Museum Purchase Grant Fund

F1970-15

DAVID HOCKNEY (born 1937)

Figures With Still Life (from `The Blue Guitar') 1976-77

Hard and soft ground etching with drypoint (edition of 200)

42.5 x 34.5 cm

Purchased in 1977 with the assistance of the Victoria and Albert
Museum Purchase Grant Fund

F1977-71(10)

DAVID HOCKNEY (born 1937)

Le Plongeur (Paper Pool #18) 1978

Coloured and pressed paper pulp on paper

two sections each 182 x 213.5 cm

Purchased in 1979 with the assistance of the Victoria and Albert Museum Purchase Grant Fund

F1979-22

David Hockney first studied at the Bradford College of Art and then moved to the Royal College of Art where he soon became closely identified with 60s British 'Pop' art. Many of his works at this period have a narrative content, making them particularly popular and accessible. Hockney has lived mostly in the USA since 1964 and it was here that he became fascinated by swimming pools, producing some of his best known works in a variety of media.

Hockney's enormous output encompasses drawings, paintings, designs for opera, photo-collages and prints. The latter include etchings and lithographs as well as manipulated images using the photocopier and fax machine. A lasting preoccupation with notions of surface and depth, of artifice and naturalism, has led him through painting to photography and on to new paintings and prints which contain both abstract and figurative elements. Matisse and Picasso have remained important influences.

CK

HOWARD HODGKIN (born 1932)

David's Pool 1985

Etching and aquatint with hand-colouring (edition of 100)

64 x 79 cm

Purchased in 1987 with the assistance of the Victoria and Albert Museum Purchase Grant Fund

F1987-82

Hodgkin studied at Camberwell School of Art and the Bath Academy of Art. He has taught at Bath and also at Chelsea College of Art while exhibiting internationally. The exhibition `Howard Hodgkin Paintings' was curated and shown at the Modern Art Museum, Fort Worth, Texas and in London at the Hayward Gallery in 1996. Hodgkin's paintings and prints are a mixture of reality, memory and abstracted shapes, fused into elaborate, assymmetrical patterns of strong decorative colours, the images relating to people and relationships. The finished works are frequently reminiscent of Indian miniatures. **David's Pool** was exhibited at the Ninth British International Print Biennale.

CK

YOSHI-IKU (1824-1895)

Sanada Yoshitada overcoming Matano Kagehisha before a waterfall c.1850

Woodcut 35 x 24 cm

Presented by R.M.Priestman in 1960

F1960-31(1)

This tour de force of the Japanese Ukiyo-e woodcut depicts a battle at the bottom of a waterfall. Sanada Yoshitada and Matano Kagehisha, two warriors of the 12th century, are wrestling over Kagehisha's wakizashi, or short sword. Yoshi-iku was a pupil of the celebrated artist Kuniyoshi.

SM

ROY LICHTENSTEIN (born 1923)

Peace Through Chemistry 1970

Lithograph and screenprint (edition of 32) 97 x 157.5 cm

Purchased in 1971

F1971-45

Roy Lichtenstein has been closely identified with the American `Pop' art movement of the 1960s. He studied at Ohio State University, Columbus before teaching and working as a freelance designer and painter. In 1961 he developed his trademark style, based on advertising illustrations, comic strip characters and everyday objects. His technique grew out of newspaper enlargements, where he used the blown up dot of the reprographic process to `colour' his flat, airbrushed surfaces. Lichtenstein's images have crossed easily into the print medium and he continues to produce screenprints and lithographs with Gemini GEL in California. **Peace Through Chemistry** was exhibited in the Second British International Print Biennale in 1970.

CK

LAILA RAHMAN (born 1966)

The Worshippers Dance 1993

Etching and Aquatint 40 x 39.1 cm

Purchased 1995

F1995-12

In this etching a series of classically rendered figures with uplifted arms reach out to what appears to be a fiery sun. This massive orb has an heraldic emblem of flame and flowers at its apex. The undulating arms of the figures mirror the tongues of flame emanating from the sun. Their naked state heightens their vulnerability as they stretch towards the energy above. The figures are sexless and apparently headless. Their yearning quality contrasts with the formal quality of the work. Laila Rahman trained at the National College of Arts, Lahore and at the Slade School in London.

NPS

MICHAEL ROTHENSTEIN (1908-1993)

New York 1973

Screenprint and relief print (edition of 75)   65 X 53.5 cm

Commissioned for the Fourth British International Print
Biennale in 1974

F1976-57

Michael Rothenstein began to explore relief printing with the innovative S W Hayter in Paris during the 1950s. By the 1960s he was working with large scale wood and linocuts, often using accident and improvisation to produce adventurous results. He freely mixed processes, moving with ease between abstraction and photo-based imagery, pioneering the use of found objects such as driftwood or metal directly impressed onto paper.

Rothenstein's ground-breaking techniques reached an international audience through numerous articles, books and exhibitions. He was closely associated with the British International Print Biennale.

CK

EDWARD WADSWORTH (1889-1949)

Bradford: View of a Town 1914

Woodcut 15 x 10 cm

Purchased in 1990 with the assistance of the Victoria and Albert
Museum Purchase Grant Fund and the Friends of Bradford Art
Galleries and Museums

F1990-7

Born in Cleckheaton near Bradford, Wadsworth first studied engineering draughtsmanship in Germany. His love of hard, mechanical shapes appears in many of his works. Against the wishes of his family, he turned to art. He studied first at Bradford School of Art and later at the Slade where he joined a group of radical English artists fascinated by the developments of Cubism and Futurism on the Continent. He began to experiment with abstracted patterns of line, colour and texture.

Following the Post-Impressionist Cezanne, Wadsworth stripped away excess details in his early prints of Northern industrial towns. In **Bradford: View of a Town** the crisp technique of the woodcut emphasises the subject's bold simplicity. Bradford's chimneys and roofs are reduced to an abstracted pattern of dramatic jagged shapes.

CK

SCULPTURE

LYNN CHADWICK (born 1914)

Radar/The Politician 1953

Welded steel and stained plaster 60.5 x 49 x 28 cm

Purchased in 1983 with the assistance of the Victoria and Albert Museum Purchase Fund, the NACF and the Friends of Bradford Art Galleries and Museums

F1983-53

This piece of sculpture has now been re-titled **The Politician**. Bought for Bradford's collection with the title **Radar**, the piece recalls Herbert Read's phrase "the geometry of fear" which he had used to rationalise the return to a 'primitive' geometric abstraction in Cold War Britain of the 1950s still reeling from the horror of war-time atrocity and now combined with the new fear of the atomic bomb. Chadwick had originally trained as an architectural draughtsman and his first artworks were mobiles. He was commissioned to make three pieces for the 'Festival of Britain' in 1951. **Radar/The Politician** was one of these pieces and may originally have been intended as a model for a light fitting. Chadwick gave the piece to his friends Peter and Eileen Potworowski whose names are inscribed upon it. Potworowski was a Polish artist then living and teaching at the Bath Academy.

CAH

FRANK DOBSON (1888-1963)

Kneeling Female Nude c.1915

Sandstone 48 x 16 x 21 cm

Purchased in 1983 with the assistance of the Henry Moore Foundation

F1983-74

Kneeling Female Nude is considered one of Dobson's earliest surviving sculptures. The rough base suggests that is unfinished, perhaps abandoned when Dobson went to war in 1915.

The pose has affinities with the work of the French painter and sculptor Andre Derain, reproductions of whose work had been shown to Dobson by Wyndham Lewis. The flattened features of the face derive from African masks which were a major inflence on French artists like Derain and, particularly, Gauguin and Picasso. After seeing Gauguin's work in London in 1912, Dobson was inspired to study primitive art at the British Museum.

One of the few artists of this period not to have trained at the Slade, Dobson's art training was unusual. He first worked for two years as a studio apprentice to the traditional sculptor William Reynolds-Stephens, afterwards spending two years in Cornwall painting 'pot-boilers' of the Cornish landscape. Dobson's real training took place at art school in Arbroath, where he learned to draw from life.

CAH

ANISH KAPOOR (born 1954)

Turning the world inside out 1997

Stainless steel 148 x 184 x 188 cm

Purchased in 1997 with funding from the proceeds of the National Lottery through the Arts Council of England, the NACF and the Henry Moore Foundation

F1997.1

Anish Kapoor is regarded as one of Britain's most talented and successful sculptors with an equally eminent reputation abroad. He was awarded the **Premio Duemila** at the Venice Biennale in 1990 and the Turner Prize in 1992. He was also awarded an honorary doctorate by the University of Leeds in 1993, the first artist they had honoured in many years.

Turning the world inside out is in stainless steel, a relatively new medium for Kapoor. In the past he has used pigments of vibrant colours and other mixed media such as wood, cement, slate, sandstone, flintstone, wax, gesso and anthracite. The generative spirit pervades most of the work through the use of Hindu cosmic symbols of the male and female principle - the lingam and the yoni. The work, and the spaces around the work, are both electric and profoundly still. The colours range from the diurnal to the nocturnal. The ethereal silveriness of the aluminium and the steel used in recent works is a definite departure.

"What is most fascinating, from the transcultural point of view, in Kapoor's conflation of visual vocabularies from different times and places, is the appearance of a seamless fit on all sides. It cannot be said that the Hindu elements are primary, or the Modernist elements are. What is primary is the way the work performs its homage to various deities without seeming to betray any."

Thomas McEvilley, Venice Biennale catalogue, 1990

Turning the world inside out is a perfect shimmering globe that seems to float in spite of its immense weight. It has a presence that is at once extra-terrestrial, celestial and epic. Kapoor's preoccupation with cosmic regeneration continues. The phrase **Turning the world inside out** is charged with mythic connotations, implying searing agony, anarchy and chaos. Kapoor produces, instead, this wonderful supra-real creation. He, paradoxically, makes the internal visible, but by using impenetrable steel does not allow a glimpse of the interiorised exterior since the viewer is reflected back upon him or her self.

The sphere is unmistakeably womb-like. In the crown is a dip not dissimilar to the dip in an apple which holds the stalk or a navel depression. In Hindu creation myths Vishnu is depicted in cosmic slumber, reclining on his five-hooded serpent couch Shesha, floating on the primordial waters. From his navel emanates a stalk with a burgeoning lotus in which the four-headed god Brahma is seated. All creation seems to flow from Vishnu. Kapoor's work, too, resonates with all the weight of a creation myth.
NPS

PERMINDAR KAUR (born 1965)
Nightdress 1996
Metal and textile 147 x 107 x 13 cm (with frame)
Purchased in 1996 with funding from the proceeds of the National Lottery through the Arts Council of England
F1996-20
In the artist's own words, the function of the work is as ambiguous as the title. The metal breastplate and chainmail are the trappings of armour, not what one would wear for a peaceful night's rest. Permindar Kaur seems to be punning night with knight. She wanted to create an icon for the individual and the collective. The garment is displayed in a manner that recalls the cross. The shield is both comforting and alienating, creating a sense of security and anxiety. In its frame it seems to exist as a museum piece, associated more with the past than with the present. It also manages to be an androgynous garment. It could be a coincidence that Kaur is of Sikh descent, a faith with a warrior history forged under the Emperor Ranjit Singh (1780-1839) the Lion of the Punjab. Historically, Sikh armour includes fine examples of intricate chainmail armour. Kaur was born and educated in England and Scotland.
NPS

DHRUVA MISTRY (born 1957)
Guardian I and Guardian II 1993
Bronze (produced as maquettes for the Victoria Square commission in Birmingham; edition of 3) 35.5 x 25 x 48 cm; 35 x 27 x 47 cm
Purchased in 1996 with support from the Henry Moore Foundation, MGC/V&A Purchase Grant Fund and the National Art Collections Fund
F1996.6
Dhruva Mistry, at a relatively young age, has attained a number of impressive distinctions, commissions and exhibitions. After training at MS University, Baroda and the Royal College of Art, London, he was artist in residence at Kettles Yard Gallery, Cambridge in 1984-85. He represented Britain at the Third Rodin Grand Prize exhibition in Japan. He was elected a full member of the Royal Academy, London in 1991 and in 1993 was elected Fellow of the Royal Society

of British Sculptors.

Mistry's work is informed by an erudite reliance on the mythology and artistic traditions of a number of cultures including India and Egypt. He has been producing these eponymous Guardian figures (dvarpalas or guardians flank temple and palace entrances in India) since the 1980s in vividly painted plaster or more formal bronze or stone. These anthropomorphic figures have a presence that is at once alien and deeply familiar. Unlike Mistry's other Guardian figures these creatures are rather more androgynous. But they have the same suavity. Their faint, enigmatic smiles, the formal coquetry of the elaborately curved eyebrows emphasise their otherness, a quality that is neither benign nor inimical. They also have the protective aura of the vahans - the bird or animal vehicles of the gods that are semi-divinities in their own right. The Hindu pantheon includes guardians of the cardinal points - the North, South, West and East.
NPS

Temple Chariot Horse
Tamil Nadu early 20th century
Painted wood 218 x 215 x 95 cm
Purchased in 1997
DA14.97
The temple chariot festivals of Tamil Nadu combine drama with spectacular religious sculpture. Intricately carved chariots, some as high as three stories, are taken through the town in procession during particular festivals. The temple deity is housed within the chariot so that it serves as a mobile temple. The chariots could be drawn by as many as five hundred men. Horses such as this magnificent creature, however, are fixed to the front of the chariot in order to complete the illusion. The horse surges forward, his stance anatomically impossible, but still impressive. He is a fiery, proud beast with his flared nostrils and blazing eyes.
NPS

FRANCIS DERWENT WOOD (1871-1926)
Humanity overcoming War 1925
Serravezza marble 2.5 x 2.1 x 1.4 m
Commissioned in 1921
Two different proposals were submitted as designs for this memorial which was intended to celebrate the peace following the 'War to end all Wars'. Derwent Wood and John Havard Thomas were asked to "symbolise in sculptural form the birth of a new age, the dawn of freedom...the triumph of love over hate and malice". Derwent Wood's design was accepted and eventually sited at the rear of the Sculpture Court rather than in the centre, in order to avoid any interruption of the outline of the sculpture. The unveiling of the maquette caused major local controversy; the violence

of the image was considered inappropriate by many. Work
on the final sculpture took longer than anticipated when a
fault was discovered within the first piece of marble.
The two female figures are symbolic representations of
Humanity overcoming Bellona, wife of Mars, the god of war.
The artist cited as his inspiration, a passage from the Book
of Revelation describing an angel binding Satan in chains.
Derwent Wood was first educated in Switzerland and
Germany. On his return to England in 1889, he studied at
the National Art Training School, South Kensington. He then
became assistant to Legros at the Slade, followed by a year
as the assistant of Thomas Brock. His work was already
known in Bradford since he had sculpted the statue of Sir
Titus Salt in Saltaire in 1903.
CAH

STAINED GLASS

MORRIS, MARSHALL, FAULKNER & CO

The Tomb of Tristram and Isoude 1862

Designed by Edward Burne-Jones to illustrate the story of Tristram and Isoude from Malory's **Morte d'Arthur**

Purchased in 1916

The firm of Morris, Marshall, Faulkner & Co had been established in 1861 with the intention of revitalising British design. `Red House' had been built as a home for Morris by the architect Philip Webb in 1858 and the difficulties in finding suitable furnishings were a major factor in the later establishment of `The Firm' of `fine art workmen'.

Wiliam Morris was first introduced to Sir Thomas Malory's romantic account of the legends of King Arthur by Burne-Jones. Malory had assembled the legends in the 15th century into a two-volume prose story, published by Caxton in 1485. The scurrilous story of the love affair of Sir Tristram and Isoude is woven into the account ending with the murder of Tristram by Isoude's cuckolded husband King Mark who relents when Isoude dies of grief and allows the pair to be buried together in a tomb carved with scenes from their love story; Tristram's hunting dogs are in forlorn attendance.

MORRIS, MARSHALL, FAULKNER & CO

King Arthur and Sir Lancelot 1862

Designed by William Morris to illustrate the story of Tristram and Isoude from Malory's **Morte d'Arthur**

King Arthur and Sir Lancelot figure little in the story of Tristram and Isoude, they may, with the other portrait panel of **Queen Guinevere and Isoude** have been set slightly apart from the rest of the sequence. It has recently been suggested that King Arthur is a self portrait of William Morris.

CAH

MORRIS, MARSHALL, FAULKNER & CO

Weeping Angels 1870

Designed by Edward Burne-Jones for the east window of St James's Church, Brighouse

Presented in 1972

The central panel of Christ on the Cross is flanked by panels of mourners. To the left, the Virgin Mary is supported by Mary Magdelene and Mary, the sister of Martha, and to the right is Joseph with St John and Nicodemus. The bottom panels depict on the left, Christ blessing children and on the right the Old Testament figures Samuel and Eli.

The windows for St James's Church, Brighouse were made at the end of the Morris, Marshall, Faulkner & Co period. The overall design was probably supervised by William Morris himself; Burne-Jones was responsible for designing most of the stained glass for the firm, the figures in these panels being typical of his mature, graceful style.

The church itself, consecrated in February 1870, was the second to be built in the parish. Installed in the same year, the East window depicting the Crucifixion was placed over the altar. The West window, showing St John and St Matthew was added in 1874. Stained glass windows depicting **The Annunciation** and **The Adoration of the Shepherds** made by Charles Eamer Kempe were added in the 1890s.

St James's Church was closed in 1970 and the stained glass windows removed. The two Morris windows passed, along with the Kempe windows, to the safekeeping of Bradford Art Galleries and Museums. In 1972, they were officially presented to Bradford.

CAH

DECORATIVE ARTS

GOLD

Spiral pendant

Attributed to the Satavahana period (1st century A.D.?)

Gold Diam: 2.7 cm length with hook: 4.3 cm

Presented by the National Art Collections Fund in 1996

DA 230.96

The Satavahanas, also known as the Andhras, ruled intermittently over the Northern, and later the Western Deccan region of India between the 1st century B.C and the 3rd century A.D. They were the main conduit of goods and ideas between the North and the South. Merchants from Western Asia and the Mediterranean had trading establishments in the Satavahana kingdoms so there would have been a lively exchange of cultural influences. The Satavahanas made magnificent contributions to architecture and were responsible for the renovation and expansion of the Sanchi stupa in Central India (1st century B.C.-1st century A.D.) and the Great Stupa in Amaravati in Southern India (completed between 150 - 200 A.D.)

This exquisite little pendant is the epitome of simplicity and beautiful craftsmanship. A length of gold wire has been wound tightly round a tiny granulated gold floret. The spiral has then been encircled by very fine beaded gold edging. A long gold stem with a loop is attached to the pendant by another granulated gold floret. The granulation was probably done using acacia gum, copper oxide, malachite and gold solder. The *Gathasaptasati* an anthology said to have been composed by Hala, one of the Satavahana kings, makes reference to a variety of stones such as carnelian, jasper, and amethyst. Amulets and pendants in gold are also mentioned. Just preceding the rise of the Satavahanas there were finely crafted gold ornaments deposited in megalithic tombs in the Deccan but the spiral design of this pendant could have been derived from the spiral lintel ends of the Sanchi toranas.

NPS

Plaque depicting scene from the Ramayana

Karnataka, India 19th century

Pierced gold 8.5 x 9.8 cm

Anonymous loan

This exquisite openwork plaque depicts the worship of Rama the hero of one of Hinduism's principal epics *The Ramayana*. Sita, who would customarily have been seated beside him, is not present; however, Hanuman the monkey god is kneeling before him and the devotee at the lower left resembles the Maratha Raja Sivaji of Tanjore (1833-55). The devotee might also be the Maharaja of Mysore. The lingam in the top left corner suggests that this is a representation of the temple at Rameswaram where Rama is said to have installed a lingam in expiation for killing the demons of Ceylon. The piece may have been made in Tamil Nadu or Mysore.

NPS

Vishnu pendant

Himachal Pradesh, India 19th century

Gold with enamel 3 x 2.5 cm

Purchased in 1997

DA 10.97

This is a rare and interesting example of enamelling both in its palette and the use of cloisonné. The blue figure is that of Vishnu, one of the principal gods of the Hindu pantheon who is shown seated on a yellow lotus. The delicacy of the enamelling is particularly apparent in the green calyx.

NPS

Tali (wedding pendant)

Tamil Nadu, India 19th century,

Gold with lead backing and lac filling 2cm square

Purchased in 1993 with funding from the Friends of Bradford Art Galleries and Museums

DA 12.93

Talis are wedding pendants given by the groom's family to the bride. In some Brahmin families the bride's parents might also gift her with a tali, which she would wear on a yellow cord to distinguish it from the main tali. This tali has an image in repoussé of Hanuman the monkey god, companion and devotee of Lord Ram. Hanuman, as a bachelor, would be an unusual image for a wedding tali. It could be that he was the patron deity of the family giving the tali. The hanging loop is decorated with a small flower in granulated gold.

NPS

Tali (wedding pendant)

Tamil Nadu, India 19th century

Gold 2.2 x 0.8 cm

Purchased in 1993 with funding from the Friends of Bradford Art Galleries and Museums

DA 13.93

This wedding pendant in the form of a double shrine could only have been gifted by a family of Shaivites or Shiva worshippers. Shiva, along with Vishnu, is a major god in the Hindu pantheon. Images in repoussé of Shiva's consort Parvati and the Shiva lingam, the phallus emblem of Shiva, are placed side by side.

NPS

Tali (wedding pendant)

Tamil Nadu, India 19th century

Gold locket with lac filling 2 x 1.5cm

Purchased in 1994

DA 1.94

The shank (conch shell) and chakra (disc) images in repoussé on this pendant immediately reveal its Vaishnavite origins. Vaishnavites are worshippers of Vishnu, a major god in the Hindu pantheon. The reverse has an image in crude repoussé of what could be a nama - the trident-shape ash marking Vaishnavite worshippers wear on their foreheads.

NPS

Christian tali

Kerala, India early 20th century

Gold with rubies 3.5 x 2.5 cm

Purchased in 1997

DA 11.97

This ritual ornament is worn by married women in South India and usually is of abstract design. In this case the cross symbolises Christianity and is worn by the Christian brides of Kerala (the community are referred to as Syrian Christians) to indicate their marital status.

NPS

Christian tali

Kerala, India early 20th century,

Gold 2.5 x 1.0 cm

Presented anonymously in 1997

DA 12.97

The tali is a ritual ornament worn by married women in South India. The shape of the cross in applied gold decorates this Christian tali.

NPS

MAH RANA (born 1964)

His n' Hers 1995

Gold and steel

Pendant: 4.6cm

Necklace circum:61.2 cm

Domed cage: 3.4 x 8 cm

Drum cage: 4 x 7.6 cm

Purchased in 1996 with funding from the proceeds of the National Lottery through the Arts Council of England

DA 117.96

His n' Hers and **I Never Promised You a Rose Garden** were Rana's tongue in cheek response to the theme of weddings, partly inspired by the 19th century South Indian gold pendants in the Bradford collection. A pair of gold wedding rings are secured in two gold wire cages made from melted down second-hand wedding rings. One caged ring can be worn as a pendant. Although titled **His n' Hers** these two, beautifully crafted, pieces are deliberately made interchangeable. Rana who was born and educated in Britain, cites sculpture, not other jewellery, as her major source of inspiration.

NPS

Box

Partabgarh, India 20th century

Gold glass and white metal 3.2cm x 8.4cm x 5.8cm

Purchased in 1996

DA 180.96

In the 19th century, the towns of Partabgarh in Southern Rajasthan and Indore and Rutlam in Madhya Pradesh were well-known for their method of producing jewellery of chased gold on coloured glass. The goldsmiths made ornaments of gold and silver on glass. Thin, perforated decorative gold forms are fused onto sheets of coloured glass with a blowpipe. The motifs were taken equally from Hindu mythology and from Mughal courtly hunting scenes. The glass is either blue, green or red and is usually taken from the windows of defunct palaces. Older items tend to be made of much thinner green glass. This box has a lid in red glass with an intricate peacock figure with spread tail in chased gold.

NPS

Comb

Partabgarh, India 20th century

Glass, gold and shell 11.3cm x 3cm x .9cm

Purchased in 1996

DA 181.96

The spine of the comb has delicate gold floral tracery over deep blue glass. The teeth of the comb, also an attractive deep blue, is probably made from shell.

NPS

Four rings

Partabgarh, India 20th century

Gold, glass and white metal   between 1.5cm x 2cm & 1.8cm x 2cm

Purchased in 1996

DA 182.96 - 186.96

The rings are decorated with floral and bird motifs.

NPS

Set of goldsmith's moulds

Deccan and Himachal Pradesh, India late 19th-early 20th century

Cast brass and bronze

Family group: 2 x 3.5 cm

Ganesh: 4.5 x 4.5 cm

Fish: 2 x 3.2cm

Symbolic motifs: 1.2 x 10.8 cm

Peacock: 3.5 x 3.7 cm

Floral & plant motifs: 6.8 x 7.5 cm

Purchased in 1996

Numerous replicas of an image can be produced by using such deeply incised moulds. Sheet gold or silver would be hammered into the pre-existing shapes. These moulds are miniature works of art in their own right and depict a variety of plant, animal and figurative forms. This group of six moulds depict auspicious and religious motifs such as figures of Ganesh, the elephant-headed god, fish and symbolic motifs.

NPS

SILVER

Shrine

Rajasthan, India early 20th century

Silver with coloured glass beads 47 x 36.5 x 28 cm

Purchased in 1995 with funding from the Friends of Bradford Art Galleries and Musuems

DA 38.95

The minimal technology and expert craftsmanship used in this miniature mobile shrine typifies the nature of silver crafting in India. No heat, for instance, has been used in the constructing or assembling of the shrine. The image of the deity would have been placed on the double-stepped shrine which is backed by a sheet of arched silver with embossed roses, trailing leaves and a central sun-burst pattern, further flanked by two female attendants carrying chauris, the sacred whisk made of yak-tail hair. The shrine is surmounted by a detachable, silver chatri or ceremonial parasol with pendant silver links and glass beads. The floor of the shrine is of ring-matted silver.

NPS

Shank (Conch shell)

Rajasthan, India early 20th century

Incised silver and shell 20 x 7 x 7 cm

Purchased in 1995 with funding from the Friends of Bradford Art Galleries and Museums

DA 35.95

Conch shells are an important part of Hindu pujas or ritual worship. The deep, resonant sound they produce when blown emphasises the sacred nature of the occasion. As an emblem of Vishnu, one of the principal gods in the Hindu pantheon, conch shells were used as containers with which to lustrate Vishnu. The solid silver casing of this shell has a delicate punched design of loops and leaves with the initials AKRI on the spiral with a spray of incised and punched flowers on the body.

NPS

Pandan (Betel leaf-server)

Rajasthan, India late 19th or early 20th century

Perforated silver 28.5 x 22.5 x 21 cm

Purchased in 1996

DA 158.96

The eating of pan is a ritual in itself, and at its height, was an elaborate ceremony, not unlike Japanese tea-drinking ceremonies, in aristocratic or wealthy Indian homes. The various implements used in the preparing and serving of pan could be beautiful works of art in their own right. Often ingenious devices were used to store the various ingredients. Pan consists of the aromatic betel leaf into which is folded crushed areca or betel nut, sugar, lime paste (sometimes mixed with narcotics) and spices. The leaf would be folded into a neat triangle and held in place by plugging a whole clove through it. Pan is used as an after-dinner digestif. It is also part of the `sringar' ritual -preparing the toilette for a lover, since it perfumes the breath. This triangular-shaped pandan is a beautiful example of silver craftsmanship and is in four sections. The perforated decoration of the sides and lid depicts a delicate floral tracery and the auspicious Hindu symbol of Aum. The lid contains a number of receptacles for the various ingredients of pan. The domed handle of the lid is itself a container for the lime paste. The main body of the container would be a storage place for the pan leaves.

NPS

Cosmetics box

South India late 19th or early 20th century

Silver, gilt and turquoise 8.2 x 11.2 cm

Purchased in 1996

DA 162.96

The central flower unscrews to enable the four lids of the flower-shaped box to open like extended petals. The box stands on delicate lion feet. Turquoises are set in tiny flower-shaped mounts on each section of the top.

NPS

Cosmetics box

Rajasthan, India early 20th century

Silver 4.5 x 8.6 cm

Purchased in 1996

DA 163.96

This flower-shaped box has six compartments with heart-shaped lids. The central handle unscrews to enable the lids to be lifted by curved leaf-shaped handles. The box stands on three tiny ball feet.

NPS

Attardan (Perfume container)

Rajasthan, India late 19th or early 20th century

Silver with gilt 17 x 17.5 cm (when open)

Purchased in 1996

DA 144.96

The silver globe is surmounted by a silver bird which when depressed, opens the globe into two halves. These reveal a gently golden interior with four silver perfume containers held in coronet-shaped fixings. The lids have tiny spoons attached. Traditional Indian perfumes, which are oil-based and rich, are distilled from sandalwood, jasmine and roses. Their evocative fragrance was an important element in 'sringar' the preparation of the toilette before meeting a lover. These perfumes are not as popular as they once were.

NPS

Parrot feeder

Gujarat, India late 19th or early 20th century

Perforated and cast silver 26 cm x 28.5cm

Purchased in 1996

DA 154.96

This delightful bird-feeder might be free-standing or suspended on a balcony or a terrace (brass versions are suspended from tree branches. This would enable pet birds to perch and feed from seed placed in the circular high-sided tray or sip water from the two small silver containers. The solid silver handle is ornamented by sculpted silver parrots.

NPS

CERAMICS AND GLASS

KALIM AFZAL (born 1966)

Fountain 1996

Glass 104 x 53.5 x 53.5 cm

Purchased in 1996 with funding from the proceeds of the National Lottery through the Arts Council of England

DA 98.96

Mughal and Rajput miniatures often depict fountains with graceful spumes of water. Kalim Afzal who has travelled widely in the continent, was also attracted by the fountains found in formal gardens in Italy and Spain. Other, more direct, sources of inspiration for this beautiful functional fountain include the Moorish tiered bronze hanging lamps of Granada. The amethyst coloured glass has ruby streaks. The play of light and water on glass creates a fairy-tale effect.

Afzal has adapted a little-used Swedish technique called graal for the making of this fountain which allows for the fusing of two colours. Afzal was born and brought up in Bradford and currently lives in Buckinghamshire.

NPS

LORETTA BRAGANZA

Elemental Vessels 1996

Slab-built ceramics, decorative slipware

(1) 28.7 x 33 cm

(2) 16.6 x 21.8 cm

(3) 1.3 x 2 cm

Purchased in 1996 with funding from the proceeds of the National Lottery through the Arts Council of England.

DA 12-14.96

The three asymmetrical pots are in pinks, yellows, blues, greens and browns over black ground. Braganza, who was born in India, is influenced by a whole range of pot forms including the Indian hundi and lota. She tends to produce pots that relate together in familial groups but also have their own autonomy. These three pots, however, work best as a group. Braganza's earlier pots had a severe, classical symmetry and an anthropomorphic aspect. These pots suggest rocks and pebbles, the mark-making recalling the marking of time and weather. The slips are subtle and ever-changing in the light and range from the autumnal to the misty.

NPS

LUBNA CHOWDHARY (born 1964)

Cartwright Hall 'Bradford City' (series of nine architectural landmarks of Bradford) 1995

Stoneware glazes with oxides 32 x 31 x 18 cm

Purchased in 1995 with funding from the proceeds of the National Lottery through the Arts Council of England.

DA 2.95

Bradford City is a series of nine sculptural ceramics based on the architectural landmarks of Bradford. This work is a deliberate departure from Lubna Chowdhary's earlier pieces where organic shapes such as the pod and the shell dominated along with odd , spiky architectural constructs. Chowdhary has worked much more directly from the buildings in order to make them identifiable. However, there has been a distillation and the features she has retained are the ones she considers give each building its character. Quirkiness is not completely absent and all the buildings stand on little feet. They have the fine detailing of ivory combined with a child-like naivety, reinforced by the fact that they are deliberately not to scale.

Lubna Chowdhary was born in Tanzania and came to Britain at the age of five.

NPS

HENRY PIM (born 1947)

Two vases 1984

Slab built stoneware, 62 x 30 x 12 cm each

Presented by the Contemporary Art Society in 1986

D/64/86/1-2

Henry Pim's usual method of production is slab-building. These stoneware vessels are textured with the use of stamps and by throwing pieces of clay onto patterned plaster of Paris bats. The slabs are cut to shape from a curved surface then joined to make the form. The distinctive form and texture are complemented by the colour of the pink and blue stoneware glazes used. A cobalt blue glaze has been used to coat the recessed areas to accentuate the surface texture.

NM

PRISCILLA MORGAN-HILL (born 1965)

Three glass vessels 1996

H:29 cm, Circum:56.5 cm

H:31.5 cm, Circum:46 cm

H:30 cm, Circum:54.5 cm

Purchased in 1996 with funding from the proceeds of the National Lottery through the Arts Council of England

DA227-229.96

Priscilla Morgan-Hill uses the fluidity of hot glass to sculpt it into amorphic forms. The black specked surface is engraved and cut through to reveal rich, jewel-like colours. She sees her work as charting the journey of her birth in East Africa, childhood in the Seychelles, maturity in South Africa and

settlement in England. This is reflected through the link between the human form and the vessel. Morgan-Hill currently lives and works in France.

NPS

TEXTILES

Wall-hanging

Turkey 19th century

Satin-silk with gold and silver thread 266 x 182 cm

DA129.96

This splendid textile in ivory, crimson and green is lavishly embroidered in gold and silver thread. The central panel of crimson ground contains calligraphic motifs and the surrounding petal-shaped panels in alternating ivory and green also have calligraphic and foliate motifs. The highly stylised rendering of the calligraphy makes it impossible to decipher. It suggests the tugrah shape for which Turkish calligraphers were famous. Tugrahs, a uniquely Ottoman creation, were stylised monograms that were equated with royal seals. There were specially created tugrahs for each and every official document comprising letters compacted to form a distinctive shape that towered over the rest of the writing on the page. Each sultan had his own tugrah. The date embroidered on this tugrah is Hijra 1125 which would imply it was from the early 18th century. This is, however, highly unlikely.

The cross inset within the crescent moon could mean that this was the work of a Christian craftsman. It is also possible that the hanging was intended for an overseas market rather than a Turkish household.

NPS

Dastarkhan (carpet or floor cloth)

Machlipatnam, Andhra Pradesh 19th century

Fine cotton chintz with block printing 300 x 132 cm

Purchased in 1993

DA 8.93

A dastarkhan would be used as a carpet covering on which food would be served. The block-printing, using vegetable dyes in red, blue, green, fawn and black is of very fine quality. Tea, henna, pomegranate and iron filings would have been used to produce the colours. The central panel has floral designs and the borders have stylised floral panels enclosing cartouches with Persian couplets. The gist of the couplets is:

O you the spreading-out of whose tablecloth is exalted.

and

O you, of whose banquet of generosity is time (or destiny)

NPS

Sari

Benares 19th century

Navy silk with gold, green, cerise and white brocading

510 x 114.5 cm

Purchased in 1993 with support from the MGC/V&A Purchase Grant Fund

DA 1.93

This sari is unusually heavy because of the quality of the gold zari used for the brocading. The ground cloth of navy silk has floral gold zari motifs. The edges are cerise and navy-blue with floral motifs and vivid green parrots. The pallav or end-cloth is made up of fine gold lines and motifs echoing the sari edges.

NPS

Sari

Varanasi 19th century

Brocaded silk 464 x 109 cm

Purchased in 1993 with support from the MGC/V&A Purchase Grant Fund

DA 5.93

The ground cloth of crimson silk is brocaded with a gold zari grid design with a small trefoil motif within each square. The edges have plain gold bands woven in a chevron design edged with broken black lines.

NPS

Phulkari

Punjab early 20th century

Cotton with floss silk embroidery 213.5 x 122 cm

DA 130.96

Phulkaris and Baghs or 'flowering work' and 'gardens' are a sophisticated domestic embroidery tradition practised in the Punjab, particularly by Sikhs. They were usually part of a bride's trousseau or a gift to a shrine and were used as hangings, coverings or part of a bride's apparel. Both friends and relatives would work collectively on each piece. This embroidery tradition flourished in the 19th and early 20th centuries, although it is still produced today for a more commercial market.

This delightful phulkari has a tan cotton ground divided into panels by bands of cross stitch. Each panel is embroidered with a different motif using yellow, green, magenta and purple silk threads. Each motif is outlined in white backstitch and the designs filled in with satin stitch. The animals include horses, camels, elephants, cattle and dogs, affectionately regarded as friends and hunting companions. The birds include parrots, pigeons and peacocks. The figures represent domestic scenes, a pair of women dancing, men wrestling, a woman churning butter, a man listening to a horn gramophone and a bullock carriage. Other items include bottles, a cooking pot and a shrine. The

sides are bordered with bold, stylised flowers and leaves.

NPS

Guru Nanak with his two companions

Ahmedabad, Gujarat early 20th century

Silk with silk embroidery 68.5 x 73 cm

Presented by Cougar Freight Services in 1996

DA 216.96

This rare textile, although produced in Gujarat, would have almost certainly been commissioned by a Sikh, probably one of the small number based in Ahmedabad since the 19th century. Embroidered in fine chain and satin stitch on to a mauve silk background are Guru Nanak, the first Guru and founder of Sikhism (1469-1539). He sits facing his two companions Bala and Mardana. A bird in a cage is suspended from a nearby tree, while exquisitely embroidered blossoms scatter the foreground. The rather stylised depictions of the three figures may have been taken from woodblock prints popular among Sikhs in the Punjab and particularly prevalent in the Punjab since the 1890s. The fineness of the embroidery is typical of Mochi (cobbler) embroideries. These beautiful pieces were produced particularly in the 19th and early 20th century, using a cobbler's awl instead of a needle.

NPS

SARBJIT NATT (born 1962)

Mughal 1996

Silk textile dyes and handpainting on silk 168.5 x 110 cm

Purchased in 1996 and funded from the proceeds of the National Lottery through the Arts Council of England

DA 221.96

Natt's work has often been inspired by Indian textiles, particularly phulkaris, and traditional Indian architecture. In **Mughal** the horizontal panels are filled with distinctive architectural details and shapes in subtle colours, which seem suffused with warm light. In the upper section is a strip of sky or water in shades of green from pale jade to chartreuse to deep bottle green with a further panel of architectural forms above.

NPS

NINA EDGE (born 1962)

Zero 1996

Batik on cotton 239 x 223 cm

Purchased in 1996 and funded from the proceeds of the National Lottery through the Arts Council of England

DA 222.96

Nina Edge uses batik to convey philosophical and radical messages. The accessibility of the medium appeals to her, since it is practised by professionals and amateurs alike. The concept of zero was invented and evolved by Indian thinkers and had entered the written language by the 6th century.

"The word language developed to encompass zero has informed the appearance of this work. A fabric, itself a mathematical puzzle of visible woven strands, is covered with marks devoid of pigment, so nothing marks the image out, in a sea of infinite blue. The empty spaces on this fabric imply the now invisible rope of geometry, and confirm that nothing is invisible, without something to measure it by. Sky, empty, void, complete, stars are some of the many words which described zero, before it became the dot and then the circle by which we now recognise the value of nothing; the reservation empty space". Edge lives in Liverpool.

NPS

FAHMIDA SHAH (born 1966)
Untitled 1996
Silk with textile dyes and handpainting 209.5 x 112 cm
Purchased in 1996 and funded from the proceeds of the National Lottery through the Arts Council of England
DA115.96
Fahmida Shah's sumptuous, silk hangings are often inspired by architectural features, usually abstracted beyond recognition. In this piece, Shah was influenced by the massive grandeur of Cartwright Hall Art Gallery itself. She found the imposing nature of the building to be in stark contrast to an exhibition on show, during her visit, a survey on heavy metal culture entitled Sound and Fury. The fluid nature of a contemporary theme with Harley Davidson motorbikes, neo-gothic art, body ornaments and large mask-like faces was balanced by the solidity of the traditional architecture. All of Shah's textiles are characterised by the use of vibrant colours and spatial arrangements.

Shah was born in Pakistan and lived briefly in East Africa before her family moved to Britain. Her frame of reference and her sources of inspiration, therefore, span three different continents.

NPS

GLOSSARY

al Asma al Husna
The 99 most beautiful names of Allah

Attardan Perfume container

Basmala The opening verse of every sura in the Quran, `Bismi'llahi 'l-Rahmani 'l-Rahimi' is in its entirety referred to as the Basmala.
Most people, however, refer to it as the Bismila or the Bismillah.

Bat Usually made from a block of plaster of paris and used for the preparation of clay and the application of texture onto slabs of clay

Batik Textile printing, originated in Indonesia. The design is marked out in wax so that when the fabric is dyed the waxed sections do not take the dye.

Bidri Metalworking technique taking its name from Bidar, in the Deccan, describing objects made from zinc alloy which is blackened and inlaid with silver on brass or both.

Burin A scratching tool used in print-making

Chandi The moon

Chatri Ceremonial parasol; a small partition or kiosk on the roof of a building

Chikan kari
Embroidery in white cotton thread on muslin or cotton.

Collyrium Kohl

Doopdan Receptacle for incense

Euston Road School
A group of British artists in the 1930s who took their name from Euston Road, London. William Coldstream, Laurence Gowing, Victor Pasmore and Claude Rogers were the most important artists.

Granulation
A technique of bonding minute spheres of gold to a gold surface, which reached its highest level of perfection under the Etruscans. It seems to have had a continuous history in India, unlike the West where the technique died out until revived in the mid 19th century.

Gulabpash Rosewater sprinkler

Gurdwara Holy place of worship for the Sikhs

Hanuman The monkey-god, son of Vayu the god of wind

Hookah A type of pipe where tobacco smoke is bubbled through water.

Ikat A weaving process where sections of the warp or weft threads are resist-dyed before weaving to a programmed pattern. In double ikat both the warp and weft threads are resist-dyed

Intaglio Engraved design or incised carving

Inro A small box of several sections, holding Taoist medicines. Inro are held together by a cord which hangs from the belt, or *obi*, of Japanese traditional dress.

Jahangir (r.1605-27) son of the Mughal emperor Akbar and father of Shah Jahan

Jali An architectural term where marble, stone or wood is pierced in geometric or arabesque patterns.

Kabuki Popular Japanese theatre (as opposed to the classical Noh theatre). Kabuki was a fusion of acting and dance, in which the female parts were played by young men. Kabuki has overtones of decadence and dubious morality.

Kalamkari Literally translated from Persian, it means penwork. Refers to painted and printed textiles. A pen or brush is used to apply mordants or liquid wax as a resist onto textiles. Particularly flourished and continues in Machlipatnam in Andhra Pradesh in India.

Kalighat art A school of painting with religious and, later, social themes that flourished approximately from 1800-1930 in Kalighat, Calcutta. Characterised by strong colours and vigorous line.

Kantha Quilted coverlet; in Bengal it refers particularly to domestic embroidery of the 19th and 20th century

Lakshmi The consort of Vishnu and the goddess of wealth

Leading The strips of lead which hold together the 'jigsawed' sections of stained and coloured glass.

Lingam Also known as linga. Phallic symbol of Shiva

Makara A mythical water beast

Mochis Members of the cobbler community

Mughal Turko-Persian Muslim rulers of India from the 16th century

Navratna — Nine gems, usually diamond, sapphire, ruby, emerald, pearl, coral, chrysoberyl, zircon and topaz or moonstone. Each stone relates to a particular planet and in conjunction they are supposed to have talismanic power

Netsuke — A toggle, usually made of wood or ivory, tied to the cord of the *inro* or other sagemono (literally, 'hanging things' - purses, tobacco pouches etc). Netsuke were often masterpieces of miniature carving.

New English Art Club (NEAC) — A group of British artists who had mostly trained in France joined together in the 1880s as an alternative to The Royal Academy. Most are now more popularly known as British Impressionists. Henry La Thangue and George Clausen were among the most important.

Pandan — Container in which ingredients such as betel-leaves, areca nuts, spices and lime paste are stored.

Pan-leaves — From the Betel plant wrapped around chopped areca nuts, spices and lime paste and chewed as a digestif

Panch Patra — Ritual vessel of silver or steel in which five (panch) sacramental foods are mixed, yoghurt, milk, clarified butter, honey and sugar lumps and served to worshippers after puja

Parvati — Consort of Shiva and mother of Ganesh

Patuas — Scroll (pat) painters from rural Bengal. Their forceful imagery can be seen in Kalighat paintings as well as in the work of Jamini Roy.

Phulkari — Colourful and intricately embroidered textiles originating from the Punjab in India. When the cloth is completely covered with embroidery it is referred to as Bagh.

Plein air — (In the open air) The practice of painting out of doors in order to achieve naturalistic effects in landscape. An ideal derived from the French realist painter Bastien-Lepage taken up with enthusiasm by many British Impressionist painters.

Puja — Hindu ceremony of public or private worship

Rama — Hero of the Hindu epic *Ramayana*. Embodiment of good.

Ramayana — One of the two main Hindu epics, the other being the *Mahabharata*

Rangoli — Auspicious floral, geometric and figurative floor-paintings of rice flour or chalk. Decorates front of house or temple

Repousse — (From the French 'thrust back') in relief on thin metal beaten up from the reverse side.

Rumi — Jalul-Din-Rumi (1207-1273) was a Sufi mystic poet from the northern Iranian province of Khorasan. He became a prominent theologian, teacher and poet.

Shiva — One of the principal gods of the Hindu pantheon

Sikh — Disciple. Adherent of the religion, founded by Guru Nanak (1469-1539)

Simurgh — A mythical phoenix-like bird of Iranian legend

Sindoordan — Container for vermilion powder used to decorate forehead

Sita — Heroine of the *Ramayana* and Rama's wife; she is seen as the embodiment of purity

Sringar — One of the nine rasas or emotional modes. Refers to the erotic

Stoneware — A term used to describe pottery which is fired to a high temperature making the clay hardened and non-porous

Sumo — A form of wrestling. Sumo wrestlers use a combination of their great bulk, strength and agility to make their opponents fall, or to push them out of the circular arena. Matches between two stables of Sumo wrestlers take place over several days

Surahi — Container for water

Surmadan — Container for surma; a grey-blue kohl, particularly favoured by Muslims

Swadeshi — Indigenous, produced in the country. A resistance movement initiated by Gandhi during the struggle for Indian Independence.

Sutradhara — Holder of the thread

Tali — Small gold convex pendants worn by wife as long as the husband is alive. Symbolises marriage.

Tugrah — Calligraphic royal seal used by Turkish sultans

Vahan — A vehicle for Hindu gods; usually bird or animal

Vishnu — One of the principal gods of the Hindu pantheon

Wasli — Piece of wood, parchment, paste-board, or slate: from wasl (Urdu) meaning connection, meeting, marriage; patch or addition as in lamination

Zari — Gold or gold-plated silver wire with a silk core used for brocaded textiles.

BIBLIOGRAPHY

Araeen, Rasheed; 1989. **The Other Story**: Hayward Gallery, London (exhibition catalogue).

Asahi, Akira and Kumagai, Isako and Kaai, Harvo; 1981. **The World in Contemporary Prints 1955-1980**: Tokyo Metropolitan Art Museum.

Bayly, Christopher; 1990. **The Raj: India and the British: 1600 - 1947**: National Portrait Gallery, London.

Carey, Frances and Anthony Griffiths; 1990. **Avant-Garde British Printmaking 1914-1960**: British Museum Publications, London.

Chakravorty, Gayatri Spivak;1988. **In other Worlds**: Routledge, London.

Chakravorty, Gayatri Spivak;1990 **The Post Colonial Critic**: Routledge, London.

Fehervari, Geza and Y.H. Safadi; 1981. **1,400 Years of Islamic Art**: Khalili Gallery, London.

Fellows, R.A; 1985. **Sir Reginald Blomfield: an Edwardian Architect**: London. Zwemmer.

Fellows, R.A; 1995. **Edwardian Architecture: Style and Technology**: Lund Humphries Ltd, London.

Garton, Robin and various; 1993. **British Printmakers 1855-1955**: Scolar Press in association with Garton & Co., Aldershot.

Gilmour, P; 1970. **Modern Prints**: Studio Vista, London.

Gilmour, P; 1978. **The Mechanical Image: An Historical Perspective on 20th century prints**: Arts Council of Great Britain (exhibition catalogue).

Godfrey, Richard T; 1978. **Printmaking in Britain: A General History from its Beginnings to the Present Day**: Phaidon, Oxford.

Goodhart-Rendel, H.S; 1953. **English Architecture since the Regency: an Interpretation**: Constable, London.

Guy, John and Deborah Swallow; 1990. **Arts of India 1550-1900**: Victoria and Albert Museum, London.

Hardman, Malcolm; 1986. **Ruskin and Bradford: An Experiment in Victorian Cultural History**: Manchester University Press, Manchester.

Healey, E; 1885. **A Series of Picturesque Views of Castles and Country Houses in Yorkshire**: compiled from the Bradford Weekly Telegraph.

Herrmann, Frank; 1972. **The English as Collectors**: Chatto and Windus, London.

Hoare, Oliver; 1987. **The Calligrapher's Craft**: Ahuan Gallery of Islamic Art, London.

Jain, Jyotindra; 1982. **The Master Weavers**: Government of India, New Delhi.

Jayakar, Pupul and various; 1982. **Aditi**: Festival of India, London.

Khanna, Balraj; 1993. **Kalighat: Indian Popular Painting 1800-1930**: Redstone Press, London.

Khatibi, Abdelkebir and Sijelmassi, M; 1976. **The Splendour of Islamic Calligraphy**: Thames and Hudson, London.

Laidlay, W.J; 1907. **The Origin and First Two Years of the New English Art Club**: 'The Author', London.

Lewison, Jeremy; 1990. **Anish Kapoor, Drawings**: Tate Gallery Publications, London (exhibition catalogue).

Lewison, Jeremy (ed); 1990. **A Genius of Industrial England, Edward Wadsworth 1889 - 1949**: Lund Humphries, London (exhibition catalogue).

Lings, Martin; 1976. **The Quranic Art of Calligraphy and Illumination**: World of Islam Festival Illustrated Series; Scorpion, London.

Linstrum, D; 1978. **West Yorkshire Architects and Architecture**: Lund Humphries, London.

Maas, Jeremy; 1969. **Victorian Painters**: Barrie and Rockcliff, The Cresset Press, London.

MacCarthy, Fiona; 1994. **William Morris: A life for our time**: Faber and Faber Ltd, London.

McConkey, Kenneth; 1978. **A Painter's Harvest, H.H. La Thangue 1859-1929**: Oldham Art Galleries and Museums (exhibition catalogue).

McConkey, Kenneth; 1995. **Impressionism in Britain**: Yale University Press and the Barbican Art Gallery, London (exhibition catalogue).

Michell, George (ed); 1982. **In the Image of Man**: Weidenfield and Nicolson, London

Michell, George (ed); 1992. **Living Wood, Sculptural Traditions of India**: Marg Publications, Bombay.

Nabholz-Kartaschoff, Marie; 1986. **Golden Sprays and Scarlet Flowers**: Museum of Ethnography, Basel, Switzerland and Kyoto, Japan.

Nasr, Seyyed Hossein; 1976. **Islamic Science: An Illustrated Study**: World of Islam Festival Publishing Company, London.

Nowell-Smith, Simon (ed); 1964. **Edwardian England, 1901-1914**: Oxford University Press, Oxford.

Pal, Pratapaditya (ed); 1996. **Expressions and Evocations, Contemporary Women Artists of India**: Marg Publications, Mumbai.

Paley, Maureen and various; 1994. **Wall to Wall**: The South Bank Centre, London (exhibition catalogue).

Pevsner, Nikolaus; 1963. **Yorkshire, The West Riding**: Buildings of England Series, Penguin Books, London.

Poovaya-Smith, Nima; 1991. **The Circular Dance**: Arnolfini, Bristol (exhibition catalogue)

Poovaya-Smith, Nima; 1992. **101 Saris From India**: Bradford Art Galleries and Museums (exhibition catalogue)

Poovaya-Smith, Nima; 1993. **Worlds Beyond: Death and the Afterlife in Art**: Bradford Art Galleries and Museums (exhibition catalogue)

Rahman, Pares Syed Mustafizur; 1979. **Islamic Calligraphy in Medieval India**: University Press Ltd. Bangladesh

Rice, David Talbot; 1975. **Islamic Art**: Thames and Hudson, London

Robins, Anna; 1986. **The New English Art Club Centenary Exhibition**: Christies, London (exhibition catalogue)

Rothenstein, Michael; 1962. **Linocuts and Woodcuts**: Studio Books, London

Rothenstein, Michael; 1970. **Relief Printing**: Studio Vista, London

Rothenstein, William; 1931. **Men and Memories: Recollections of William Rothenstein, 1872-1922**: Volumes I & II, Faber & Faber, London

Said, Edward W; 1978. **Orientalism**: Routledge Kegan Paul, London.

Said, Edward W; 1993. **Culture and Imperialism**: Chatto and Windus, London.

Saint, A; 1976. **Norman Shaw**: New Haven, London.

Schimmel, Annemarie; 1984. **Calligraphy and Islamic Culture**: New York University Press.

Simmons, Rosemary; 1990-1997. **Printmaking Today**: Quarterly Journal of Contemporary Graphic Art. Farrand Press, London.

Singh, Kushwant, Poovaya-Smith, Nima; Ponnapa, Kaveri; 1991. **Warm and Rich and Fearless: A Brief Survey of Sikh Culture**: Bradford Art Galleries and Museums (exhibition catalogue).

Singh, Martand; Pria Devi; Kapur Rta; and Jain, Jyotindra, 1982. **The Master Weavers**: Festival of India, New Delhi.

Speight, William; 1898. **Chronicles and Stories of Old Bingley**: Elliot Scott Publications.

Stangos, Nikos (ed); 1976. **Hockney by Hockney**: Thames and Hudson, London.

Stangos, Nikos (ed); 1993. **That's the way I see it**: Thames and Hudson, London.

Stronge, Susan; Smith, Nima; Harle, J. C; 1988. **A Golden Treasury: Jewellery from the Indian Sub-continent**: Victoria and Albert Museum with Mapin Publishing, London.

Stronge, Susan (ed); 1995. **The Jewels of India**: Marg Publications, Mumbai.

Summerson, Sir J; 1976 **The Turn of the Century: Architecture in Britain around 1900, W.A. Cargill Memorial Lectures In Fine Art**: University of Glasgow Press, Glasgow.

Waterfield, G. (ed); 1991. **Palaces of Art: Art Galleries in Britain 1790-1990**: Dulwich Picture Gallery, London (exhibition catalogue).

Welch, Anthony; 1979. **Calligraphy in the Arts of the Muslim World**: University of Texas Press, Houston.

Wortley, Laura; 1988. **British Impressionism, A Garden of Bright Images**: The Studio Fine Art Publications, London.

Yorkshire Daily Observer: 1904. 13 April, Leeds William Byles & Sons, Bradford.

Zimmer, Heinrich; 1972. **Myths and Symbols in Indian Art and Civilization**: Princeton University Press, Bollingen Foundation, Washington.

Bradford Art Galleries and Museums; 1987. **Cartwright Hall: A Guide to the Building and its Architecture**, Bradford

Bradford Art Galleries and Museums; 1989. **The Connoisseur**, Bradford (exhibition catalogue)

Bradford Art Galleries and Museums; 1968-1990. **Exhibition catalogues of the British International Print Biennale**: 1968, 1970, 1972, 1974, 1976, 1979, 1982, 1984, 1986, 1988, 1990: Cartwright Hall, Bradford